THE PREEMIE PARENT'S SURVIVAL GUIDE TO THE NICU

How to Maintain Your Sanity & Create a New Normal

By

Nicole Conn & Deb Discenza

Alan R. Spitzer, M.D.
Medical Editor

second edition

The Preemie Parent's Survival Guide to the NICU was published in 2020 by PreemieWorld, LLC
P.O. Box 10733, Burke, VA 22009
www.PreemieWorld.com

Cover Photo: little man Productions
Book design by Lainie Liberti, Tuan Vu Tran, and Andrea Kuhne for jungle[8].
Production Team Manager: Bri Ziganti, Felice Media
Copy Editor: Jenny McCormick

Printed in Hong Kong
Sea-Hill Press, Inc. www.seahillpress.com
First Printing: November 2009

Printed in Canada
Premier Printing, Ltd. premierprinting.ca
Second Printing: April 2020

ISBN: 978-1-7348470-0-0

DEDICATION

From Nicole

For Nicholas:
My little man with his gigantic spirit.

And for Gabrielle:
For being my sanity, my solace, and my rock
during the crazy NICU journey.

From Deb

For Gregg & Becky:
I am so blessed to have you in my life.

For Amy R. Perlin, D.D., Senior Rabbi of Temple B'nai Shalom:
As a fellow Preemie Mom you showed me the amazing power
of the Mi Shebeirach (healing) prayer as we did Becky's naming
ceremony in the NICU.

From Deb & Nicole

For all Preemies and their Families Worldwide:
May this book give you just a little more comfort during the NICU
journey.

For the Preemie Professionals Worldwide:
Thank you on behalf of all Preemie Parents for your amazing
talents in the NICU.

THANK YOU

This book would not have been possible without an amazing team of people who helped us envision our important mission of helping preemie families thrive and as Nicole would say look "groovy" doing it.

We'd like to thank the following people for their amazing insight into the preemie parent world in the NICU:

Our Medical Editor **Alan R. Spitzer, M.D.**,
Former Senior Vice President and Director of **The Center for Research and Education at Pediatrix Medical Group**

Our Book Editor **Olivia Giovetti**

Our Book Designers from **Jungle[8]: Lainie Liberti**, Creative Director and Principal, **Andrea Kuhne** & **Tuan Vu Tran**, Designers

Our good friend **Maureen A. Doolan Boyle**, Founder & Executive Director of **Mothers of Supertwins** and Chairperson of **PreemieCare**

PERSONAL THANKS:

On a personal note we'd like to thank the following people in our lives for their love and support as this book came to be:

NICOLE:

All My Love & Gratitude To My Family:

Gabrielle – for being my bestest "Bi-Bi Bo-Bo" and forever making my heart sing

David – for your gentle nature, wicked humor and keeping me young!

Lauren – for being so smart, so very kind, and for secret candy stashes!

Alexandra – for your lyrical poetry, crazy singing, and adorable self

Daisha – for your keen wit, insight, and keeping the kids endlessly entertained!

Nicholas – for making me grateful every single day, my "little man"—my soul.

Special Thanks Always and Forever to the entire staff at **Cedars Sinai Hospital** in Los Angeles, **Good Beginnings**, **Fernanda Erlanger** and **Dorothy Williams**.

Nicholas's primary nurses—**Becky, KJ, Judy & Stephanie**.

As well as the best of home health nurses who have become our family; **Zel, "Dan-Dan," Estee, Sonnia, Maxine & Ebony, especially "Gymbee" (Genny Verdugo) and Zel Alvarez.**

DEB:

I would like to thank both my wonderful husband, **Gregg**, and my lovely daughter, **Becky** (now 16), for their enormous support and patience as this book evolved.

I am dedicating this book in loving memory to my late parents **Garcin & Barbara Kaganowich** who inspired my love of writing and helping others.

And then there are my adopted twin brothers, **Andrew & Steven Kaganowich**, who were born prematurely and are (very appropriately) Becky's co-Godfathers and doting Uncles.

I would like to send a very special thank-you to the entire team at **Fairfax Neonatal Associates**, the team that took care of my daughter in the NICU at **Inova Fairfax Hospital for Children**. Nurse **Donna Reed**, you helped us celebrate our family for the first time in the NICU with one simple baby bath. Thank you for your amazing guidance and support then and over the years.

I want to thank my PreemieWorld team for their incredible hard work on this book: **Bri Ziganti**, Designer Extraordinaire, and **Jenny McCormick**, our Amazing Assistant Editor & Social Media Mama.

FOREWORD

Many years ago, when I first decided to become a neonatologist, I had the opportunity to take my mother on a tour of the Neonatal Intensive Care Unit (NICU) at the Children's Hospital of Philadelphia, where I was Chief Resident at the time. After wandering from bedside to bedside peering at the tiny, critically ill infants on ventilators and a variety of other amazing therapies, my mother finally stopped and said to me, "This doesn't really exist, does it?" Since that day, I have recognized that parents of premature infants often react the exact same way when they first encounter the NICU. It is a place that never did exist for them previously, yet it becomes all too real once you find yourself captive there for however long your preemie remains a NICU patient.

Because the NICU is an environment that relatively few individuals ever encounter in their lifetime, it can be profoundly confusing and difficult to comprehend for even the most educated of families. All the various sights and sounds, the life-saving alarms that echo constantly, the incredible pace of activity, the barrage of information, and the very difficult decisions that are showered upon parents each day can humble even the strongest of individuals. Coping with the stresses of preemie parenthood is, quite simply, an incredible challenge, one of the most difficult that the average person will ever face in his or her lifetime. As the grandfather of two premature infants myself, I can most definitely attest to the extraordinary nature of this challenge from both the viewpoint of the physician as well as from the perspective of the family.

Guiding a family through the NICU experience, therefore, has always seemed to me to be one of the most important aspects of care that a neonatologist can offer to a parent. But with many very complicated patients to care for and a limited number of hours in the day, finding sufficient time to answer each parent's questions in detail is always problematic for the NICU physician.

Until now, few up-to-date resources have existed that the neonatologist could point to, which would allow a family to more fully understand the complex issues that constantly arise in the care of the premature infant. Fortunately, Nicole Conn and Deb Discenza, both parents of preemies themselves, have recognized this deficiency and addressed it by writing a remarkable book that, in my opinion, should be handed to every parent upon admission of their premature infant to the NICU.

Having experienced the best and the worst of the NICU themselves, they have created a manual that no mother or father of a preemie should ever be without. The book that you now hold in your hands will be of enormous value to you as you personally attempt to navigate premature infant parenthood with Nicole and Deb as your guides.

Their insightful understanding and their unswerving support will be invaluable to you until your child is ready to go home and embark upon a life outside the NICU. You could not have two better guides to show you the way.

Alan R. Spitzer, M.D.
Former Senior Vice President
and Director of The Center
for Research and Education
Pediatrix Medical Group
Photo Credit: Pediatrix Medical Group

preemieworld

CONTENTS

I.

INTRODUCTION:

THE TWILIGHT ZONE

"This isn't medicine, it's voodoo."
-Resident taking care of Nicholas

Yes, you have just entered the Twilight Zone. Because being inside a Neonatal Intensive Care Unit for the first time feels like the worst kind of science fiction: isolettes that look like pods, wires everywhere, beeping machines. Nothing can prepare you for this experience.

All Nicole can really remember from the first 24 to 48 hours of her son's life is gripping Nicholas's isolette, his eight inch long miniature being bathed in the glow of lights, strapped up to so much machinery he looked like a mini-borg. Nicole has been told that if by some miracle, he makes it past the first 48 hours it will probably be due to the "honeymoon" period thanks to the Surfactant given for his underdeveloped lungs.

"We don't want you to be giving any false hope."

Trust us, all hope fades quickly enough in this mad world; a world that seems straight out of a twisted lab-gone-bad tale. It's a world in which the young new mom stammers in disbelief ("No really, I'm just supposed to be having a baby"), certain she is in a dream. She hasn't even had her baby shower. She hasn't even started the nursery. This can't be the moment she has waited for, hungered for, planned and prayed for.

She, like you now reading, has just entered the world of the wildly unexpected. Pain and death abound here, right alongside newly minted mothers who want nothing more than to cradle their newborns to breasts. They cannot, however, because their infants scant underweight bodies are unable to hold a temperature, or their heart valves are transposed, or their intestines have grown on the outside of their bellies. Tales abound in the NICU filled with a menagerie of IUGR (intrauterine growth restriction) Preemies, preeclampsia horror stories, and chromosomally-affected newborns.

At some point, the shock and agony of your delivery will subside and you and your spouse/partner will begin to calm. At some point you will slowly begin to regain your equilibrium, and you will begin to

venture out to share with other mothers, clasp hands, and shed tears.

One cannot imagine or dream up this world; a world where parents sit endlessly, bleary-eyed, and gaunt as they peer into tiny bins of plastic, their heads snapping to the blaring monitors. You feel off balance, and even though you know you have a vague recollection of high school biology, you will soon realize it's impossible to fully comprehend the effort put into keeping your child alive.

We take it for granted that our gurgling infants will breathe enough oxygen and rid themselves of too much carbon dioxide. We never consider that every system has to be calibrated: a tweak of bi-carb here, the twisting of knobs there, not only for pressure of air into the lungs, but also for the measurements of tidal volumes and lengths of inspiration. There is a menu of electrolytes constantly on the rebound from too much this and not enough that. Blood pressure cuffs the size of miniature Band-Aids. Photo light therapy for jaundice.

You will hear the term "roller-coaster" about a hundred times a day, and possibly your tears (like ours) will come far easier than you'd like. We strongly suggest you don't hold back. Ours were a means of survival.

"The NICU is by invitation only. And it's not an invitation you want."

-Kathleen Johnson,
Primary Nurse to Nicholas

Your baby is born. Prematurely. What was supposed to be one of the happiest days of your life—the birth of your child—has turned into a surreal event. You've entered a world that will leave you under incredible stress and duress and, perhaps, forced to make life and death decisions.

Perhaps she is merely a few weeks early and all she requires are hot lights to help her with a mild case of jaundice and some therapy to properly breastfeed. Or, perhaps he is a one pound waifling, born in his 24th week. She's a 29-weeker with a congenital anomaly. They are 31-week triplets weighing between two and four pounds. You and they are all unprepared for these harsh lights, blaring monitors, shrill commands of doctors voices, chaos, and a sense of the ultimate betrayal.

Whether you live in the NICU for the next two days, weeks, or months and no matter what week or weight your baby carries with her, you have just had an infant in the NICU. Whatever the circumstances that surround your baby's birth, this will become a life altering moment.

You are about to go on the ride of your life. What may feel like the ultimate endurance race in one

moment feels like a quick sprint over a cliff without a parachute in the next. To quote Bette Davis in *All About Eve*, "Fasten your seat-belts, it's going to be a bumpy night."

The good news is that there is a way to get through this. You probably won't emerge entirely unscathed, but you will survive, even when you think that if you have to wait one more second to see your baby, one more week to hold your darling infant, go through one more interminable discussion with the doctors, specialists, and/or social workers, or have to fill out one more form, you are going to lose your mind. Permanently. But, along with this guide, the help of strangers who will become your family, and friends who will show their true mettle, you *will* make it through to the other side.

Sure, it seems like there is no possible way you're going to make it. Your head has turned into mush; your brain is on disconnect. The doctors and nurses sound like the adults from Charlie Brown, their reports and jargon coming out like "Wa-wa-waws." You feel wrecked from the hours leading up to your infant's birth and unable to comprehend the work that still lies ahead.

You want your spouse or partner near you one moment, and you want to be alone the next. You miss your children at home but cannot leave your sweet, helpless newborn alone in her isolette. You switch from being ravenously hungry to not being able to stand the sight of food. This contortion of emotions is absolutely mind-numbing. It's also absolutely appropriate.

"Being in here and watching everything you are going through is like the distillation of pain and joy in every breath."

-Visiting Friend

This is real—all too real. And what you need to do here and now is cope with this new reality. First of all, you will forget 98% of everything you are told, and probably 100% of what you will read (that's why you have this guide to turn to again and again). So here's a new rule: Ask the same question 50 different times. Ask 50 different people until you get an answer that sticks.

No one expects anything more of you. In fact the majority of nurses will tell the parent that they are going to forget almost everything they are told. No one wants you to try to be or do anything other than the parent you are right now.

So here goes. Hang tight.

ABOUT US

DEB'S TAKE:

Deb with Becky
Photo Credit: Robyn Kuniansky

My life changed irrevocably on a late summer day in September. "Gregg, I need to get to a bathroom right now."

My husband looked at me in a puzzled fashion, wondering if I had lost my mind.

"You could have told me that ten minutes ago," he noted hinting to the fact that we had just left a family outing an hour outside of town. But he did what all good dads-to-be do for their pregnant wives—he complied. What I did not want to tell him was that I had felt my bladder let go in the passenger side seat. Embarrassed, I was hoping to get into the bathroom and clean up without a lot of ribbing from the other people in the car.

All alone in a Food Lion bathroom an hour away from home, I discovered that this was not at all an accident. My water had broken at 30 weeks' gestation. I sobbed, apologized out loud to my unborn daughter and did the best I could to clean up. More fluid, more tears.

Desperate cell phone calls to a couple of people in the car did not work and went straight to voice mail. I made a plan to clean up quickly and get to the car.

On my way out of the store I stopped at the front office and clearly stated that I believed I was in preterm labor and asked where the nearest hospital was. Their jaws dropped open and they stammered out responses that they weren't from this area, so I asked to borrow the phone and promptly called my doctor.

As I did this the nice store people ran out to the car and grabbed my husband. Both he and my brother in-law rushed in as I was leaving a message with the answering service. I was in no mood to wait around for a call back. We got in the car and Gregg drove like a maniac

through snarled traffic back to the hospital where I had planned to deliver. On the way, the OB on call responded by cell phone and after quizzing me said I should probably come in and get checked. *Probably?* Good grief.

I was checked into Labor and Delivery and spent the next 30 chaotic hours fending off labor. Two lung development shots, numerous anti-labor drugs, and a five-second Lamaze lesson from an OB nurse later, Becky decided she had had enough and made her dramatic entrance into the world. I heard a tiny kitten cry and the entire team of professionals erupted in a joyous "Ohhhhh." A second later, Becky was held up to me, the only part visible was her head. For a 2 lb, 15 oz baby she somehow looked huge to me. Maybe it was my Proud Mama Hormones? We both looked at one another with a sense of "Whew!" Then she was whisked to the NICU with Gregg in tow.

A short time later I was wheeled down to the NICU on a stretcher to see Becky. I was in total shock. There on a warming table was my daughter, hooked up to all sorts of equipment and really pissed off. Exhausted and not allowed out of the stretcher, I felt unable to do anything for her. I stared with a panic stirring within me. Next thing I knew I was taken to my room, put in my bed, and told to rest.

Rest? After watching my daughter in distress and wondering if she would live? I fought off sleep as long as I could and worried endlessly. Finally, I could no longer stay awake and sent a silent prayer up to God and to my daughter's namesake before I collapsed.

The next day family and friends came by to visit. I planted a smile on my face and did the best I could. Everyone had a comment to make and it was not always appropriate. I knew they meant well and were often stymied as to what to say, but in my mind I just rolled my eyes and kept my focus squarely on Becky and Gregg.

At one point a hospital staff member came in with paperwork for me to fill out for Becky's birth certificate. As I completed it I found myself briefly hesitating at filling in Becky's intended name. Should I give her the name Gregg and I had planned on? What if she didn't survive more than a few days? I put the name down anyway. She was my Becky and nothing would ever change that. Later on that week, my rabbi came into the NICU to do Becky's naming at bedside instead of at the synagogue. A service devoted to her naming would happen much later, but right now we needed to focus on the present.

48 hours later, I was discharged from the hospital and walked out under my own power since I didn't want to wait for a wheelchair ride. Gregg pulled the car to the front door of the lobby of the women's center and loaded all of the flowers and other items from my room. Then he helped me walk down to the car. On the way, I was behind a new mom being wheeled out with her baby on her lap. With every step I found myself holding back tears as I realized that nothing was normal about this situation. As we both got into the car, Gregg and I headed home, crying all the way as we left our daughter behind in the hospital. The NICU Nurses had warned us that we would be back later that day even though we said we would not. Sure enough we went back that evening.

Visiting the NICU as the Mom was tough since I felt more like the Visitor. After scrubbing to my elbows for 2 minutes, I had to poke my hands through the portholes of the incubator just to touch my daughter. And then there was medical equipment to work around. Monitor alarms would sound and I would scream for the nurse as I watched my daughter turn blue day in and day out. Then there were the scares with heart issues as well as potential infections and more. And tests, endless tests.

Within a week, Gregg and I got to hold Becky for the very first time. Being so used to holding the huge nieces and nephews in the family, it was surreal holding my own Preemie daughter. Bundled in her blankets and medical equipment snaked around the rocking chair so I would not disconnect her, I stared down at this tiny, tiny baby. She was so light that I could barely feel her. *Be heavy, Becky. Please stay with me and be heavy.* My heart ached. She was so fragile. What had I done? And more important, what could I do for her?

Deb with 11-month old Becky
Photo Credit: Robyn Kuniansky

During this period, my mother-in-law wondered aloud when I would be able to do **Kangaroo Care**. I stared vacantly into space. Had I heard that right. Kangaroo? Where was the kangaroo? Regardless I started pestering the nurses and they finally set up me to kangaroo Becky. I was set up in a special black lounge chair and was

tilted backward, the nurse then put my daughter onto my chest. I'm sure it would be appropriate to say that I was instantly enthralled. But in reality, Becky first felt like a huge cold grasping insect. Slowly she warmed and was very still. I tried to crane my head to the side to see her face but no luck. Gregg, who was sitting beside us, had the biggest smile on his face.

"Deb you should see this. The look on her face is amazing, she is sleeping so peacefully."

Life became an endless treadmill for me as I pumped breast milk, visited Becky in the NICU, pumped breast milk, went back to work part-time one week post-childbirth, pumped breast milk, recovered from childbirth, pumped breast milk, had an ER visit due to severe postpartum bleeding, pumped breast milk, got trained on medical equipment, took a **CPR** class, prepped for the discharge, pumped breast milk, and lived through the chaos and aftermath of Hurricane Isabel. I also pumped breast milk.

Becky emerged from the NICU after 38 days and was sent home on oxygen and with an apnea monitor as well as a number of medications. We had a whole team of specialists and therapists for Becky and I still laugh at people who told me to relax because Becky was out of the hospital. If anything, I was terrified. I had to work with medical equipment and the loud alarms in the middle of the night, and watching my daughter turn blue on a dime freaked me out to no end. I had to make sure her oxygen was at just the right level and that she did not take the prongs of the nasal cannula out of her nose. Regularly, I ran through the steps for Infant CPR in case Becky had a breathing spell she couldn't shake and I was constantly afraid I would forget the steps. And when there weren't medical appointments we were basically on lockdown for the winter so Becky wouldn't get **RSV**. I felt less like a mother and more like a nurse.

Though Becky endured a readmit to the hospital, she slowly started to stabilize and thankfully shed the equipment. Life did become a bit easier. Bit by bit the doctor's appointments were shed too, but now life was filled with developmental issues and evaluations. Becky went into **Early Intervention**, later Child Find, and after that Special Education. Along the way there were the "normal" moments such as birthday parties and the first day of preschool. It was a joy to watch these moments, but also a thrill just to see Becky smile. Life was not normal. But, as with the NICU and

then the discharge period, we rolled with it and created our new normal.

Very quickly I found other local Preemie parents and was amazed at how quickly each of us connected. We told our stories and knew the others understood without too much effort. There is no pretense among Preemie moms and dads. We've been through hell and back and we tell it like it is. And I found that many of us had connected with a number of professionals in the community, especially the nurses. In a way, the professionals had taken on a family-type connotation because they witness every day the parents' stress. In talking to both parents and professionals, I have heard one common refrain: no one was prepared for this experience, and during the ordeal they were at a loss to find any sort of comfort. Mainstream parenting magazines were useless and offered no real sense of empowerment to the Preemie parent.

Life changed with Becky's early birth—and I quickly found within myself a need to help other families navigate this truly bumpy ride in the NICU and beyond. Six months after Becky's birth I left my well-paying job to conceptualize and create the hugely successful *Preemie Magazine*, a free print publication for parents and professionals. I also began providing regular speeches to the professional community and public. In the wake of this success, I found myself trying to find other ways to help families. A while later, Nicole Conn, an amazing director and author, connected with me and we excitedly discussed this book. I am proud to be continuing the much-needed work within this special community of families. Preemie parents stick together. Preemie parents need each other. And that is why we are here for you.

December, 2019—Oh how I wish I could go back a decade ago when this book was first written and tell myself it will be okay. The last ten years have been a struggle as we watched Becky enter the public school system and I had to advocate heavily with teachers, principals, special education teachers, doctors, therapists, etc. My gut instinct told me that Becky was different and I quickly learned that I was right on every single concern. My advice? Listen to your instinct and go with it until you are proven otherwise. You know your child better than any medical or educational professional. That is your superpower as a preemie parent.

—Deb

NICOLE'S TAKE:

Nicholas with Mommy CoCo
Photo Credit: Kristin Keller

It's hard to believe that, before my introduction to the NICU, I would change the channel as fast as I could if I saw a preemie on TV. I couldn't look at pictures of them in magazines. I'm ashamed to admit it, but I was terrified of them. Yet after having the smallest surviving male patient at Cedars in March 2002, I've gotten way past over it.

My partner, Gwen, and I endured the most embittered of battles that destroy the strongest of unions when our son's pregnancy de-railed. Having two people in a committed loving relationship fall so completely on opposite sides of whether to keep a pregnancy is one of the most difficult decisions any couple will ever face. Suddenly the right to life movement made more sense to me and I found myself asking questions I never thought I would remotely entertain: how one can possibly presume they know when spirit enters? And if one does feel an infant's spirit, how can they possibly terminate a pregnancy?

At the time I was working on a documentary about surrogacy. I found it fascinating to think that people could actually gestate an infant and then be able to give the baby up, but that's what was happening in our lives. Our surrogate was pregnant with our son from our frozen embryos. Unfortunately, she was also dragged into the insanity of endless specialist visits to determine the fate of our son. Initially the documentary was going to be an exploration into surrogacy, how it affects our society, how it affects our choices to even have these options, and the ramifications of such choices.

How could I know things were going to change so dramatically? When Nicholas was born by emergency C-section all I could think was: I want my son to live—no matter what

the doctors had to do; no matter what they told me the outcome might be. I already was madly in love with him, had felt his little spirit for months and knew he was a sweet soul with a gentle irony in his sense of humor.

But Nicholas's first 3 months in the **NICU** were hell. He coded multiple times, was endlessly ill with infection and sepsis, weathered one medical emergency after another, endured numerous surgeries, had more blood transfusions than could be counted, and suffered kidney failures and pulmonary hypertension. He had lost 12% of his intestines. They told me he would never get off the vent. Most of the staff still believed he wasn't going to make it out of the hospital.

My brother, Brian, had continued to shoot footage for the surrogacy documentary with the understanding that I would reconnect with the project once Nicholas was out of danger. He insisted I look at the footage he had shot and I might want to rethink what I was going to work on when we left the hospital.

Exhausted, I sat in front of the TV and what I saw was the birthing of ***little man***: the documentary I wrote and directed about Nicholas to show the raw face of prematurity and its challenges and aftermath. This was a story that had to be told. I could never have imagined that making this movie would become more an exploration into my relationship with my partner, our relationship with our daughter and son, the importance of family, and the unfathomable challenges of a premature birth.

***little man* DVD**
Copyright © little man Productions

little man went on to become a twelve-time award-winning film, was named by three different papers as one of the Top Ten Films of 2005 and had both Oscar and Emmy campaigns. I'm very proud of this documentary as a filmmaker. But I was much more touched and proud of the thousands of e-mails I received from other Preemie parents who saw the film on TV and told me they felt so validated to see their lives on the screen; no matter how much they tried to explain what it was like to be in the NICU with their baby, no one could really understand or relate to that experience. The film shows what so many of us have survived and what you are now living through.

Along the way I've had to face my own demons, examine the ramifications of willfulness, and deliberate love over denial. Making this film also became a way in which to grapple with all the feelings that comes from having faced such daunting odds (only .00004% of Nicholas's birthweight category had survived at that time) and the perpetual crisis and chaos that comes from having a medically fragile infant.

Haunted in the night by a guilt I still cannot shake, I have wondered about the cost of maintaining Nicholas's daily life. Was it okay for my son to be two years old—barely sitting—and have a **G-tub**e, oxygen line and **central line**? Was it okay for him to live at the hospital his first four years of life? What about our precious daughter, suffering because she has a baby brother with special needs? Or was this singular event in her life going to be the one thing that saved her from a pampered, coddled existence? Was this her opportunity to grow, to fiercely protect her brother, and to show a compassion way beyond her years? Did our lives make any kind of sense from the outside? Was it worth it?

After five years, my partner, with whom I had shared a wonderful life with for eleven years, determined it was not. We went through a hellacious divorce. I have heard the same story from so many other people who live this journey. The resentments are insurmountable and it becomes simply too much struggle for most relationships to endure. The focus on the medically-challenged child is the spotlight and the relationship always ends up suffering. I now have full custody of Nicholas; and Gwen and I share custody of our daughter.

After the divorce, I needed to resurrect my writing/directing career as a single mother trying to support two children, but I also wanted to do something that made a difference and supported the preemie community. I called Deb Discenza, thinking that her magazine, *Preemie Magazine*, was the ultimate

Nicholas at his favorite park
Photo Credit: Amy Hoven

resource for our community. Deb is a force of nature and her ability to do things amazes me. Both Scorpios with an insane dedication to all things Preemie, we spent the afternoon speaking in Preemie mom shorthand talking about our lives, other stories, and the future. That's when PreemieWorld.com and this book were born.

For me, yes, it has all been worth it. At the end of the day, no matter what my "little man" warrior has gone through, he calls me "flower" and "butterfly." He snuggles with me nightly, gives me the greatest kisses, and showers me with delicious smiles and a sweetness I have never experienced anywhere else. His love and soul are pure.

Clearly having Nicholas and experiencing the NICU has changed my entire life. I had spent my entire career as a filmmaker and a novelist, writing and creating stories that speak about passion and high seas romance. Never before could I dream that real life would be so much more raw and compelling.

Nicholas's spirit and sheer will to live have become my greatest strength. Every day I learn from him. His is the kind of grace under pressure that will not allow you to feel sorry for yourself. His unique gift turns medicine into miracle.

—Nicole

preemieworld

II.

HOW TO USE THIS BOOK:

THE LEGEND

Icon	Meaning
Resources	Books and Web Resources
Quotes	Quotes
Professional's Point of View	Professional's Point of View
Questions to Ask the Professional	Questions to Ask the Professional and a Place for Notes
Tips	Tips and Extras
Important Extras	Important Information
Perspective	General Perspectives
Nicole's Take	Nicole's Take
Deb's Take	Deb's Take

NICOLE'S TAKE:

When my son was born 100 days early and weighing only one pound, I was thrust into the macabre universe known as the NICU, completely and utterly lost. A pragmatic problem-solver, I still had no clue as to what world we'd walked into. I didn't understand the language; I was completely frustrated. And, because the doctors, nurses, and social workers kept reinforcing that my son could not make it with all his medical complications, I was an emotional wreck.

I searched frantically on the internet for resources, but the only books I could find were large medical tomes and memoirs filled with stories that did not end well. I was living at the hospital and hungry for information. I purchased a couple of books, and while each and every one of them had scores of valuable information, they were too overwhelming and too full of *medical-ese* for a harried mom in a whirlwind hospital room.

What I needed was this book. I needed an easy-to-understand guide that helped me navigate my way through medical terms. I needed to understand how the relationship between mom and nurse and doctor worked. I needed a friend. I needed another Preemie mom to hold my hand.

This book is not a medical information book. It will not explain to you the gestational differences between a preemie born at 28 weeks versus 34 weeks. Instead, it will guide you to the quickest way of understanding information the way we have known it from the beginning of time: alphabetically.

If you are struggling with life and death terms, the last thing you feel like doing is wading through a huge textbook. You just want to know what "ROP" means and how it relates to your baby now, this instant. And then you are probably going to forget it and need to look it up time and again. So as you see bolded terms throughout the book it should alert you to refer to the **A to Z** section to get a straightforward definition before moving forward.

But this is also not a simple glossary of terms. We also want to provide you with those crucial supporting elements that, when you have the time or the emotional stamina, allow you to understand your feelings, share other parent experiences, and get insight from doctors and nurses.

Interwoven throughout this book are sidebars, tips, resources and other useful information, as well as lists of things to consider and questions to ask doctors all enhanced by easy icons. The human touch element is provided through our personal observations as mothers under sections entitled "Deb's Take" Or "Nicole's Take." While we had extremely different experiences, between the two of us we have probably touched on every experience one can have in the NICU and can empathize with your own experiences in almost anything you'll go through during your course at the NICU.

We hope you'll find that this guide is like having another mom or dad take you by the hand, and tell you that it's okay. Every feeling, every emotion, every crazy thought you've just had, is not only absolutely valid, but perfectly normal. We also want to help you crack the "NICU Code" (those acronyms, doctors slang, and brand-names you hear incessantly), so that you can be in the know and can start a meaningful conversation with your child's team of professionals.

This book is divided into sections so that when you need something you know where to go. We put the A to Z section first so that you can learn the language of this new and foreign land one word at a time, whether it's an acronym or full-on explanation.

If you've just gotten to the NICU, you will only be able to handle bits of information here and there. It's totally normal. When you're able to assimilate more of the pieces, however, you will begin to have a more global picture of what your baby is going through and what is expected of you. If you've been sitting in the NICU for weeks, knitting your tenth blanket while going out of your mind waiting to see your infant, you might want to explore the second half of the book and check out our website at www.PreemieWorld.com.

While this will be a life-altering experience for you, it can also be filled with beauty, grace, and spiritual enlightenment. Your baby needs you. You need this book. Together we hope to walk you through to the other side. We're devoted to helping moms not just trudge through, but to become empowered advocates throughout this intense journey.

III.

THE A-TO-Z OF THE NEONATAL INTENSIVE CARE UNIT (NICU)

ACRONYMS: Learning the Lingo

ABG: Arterial Blood Gases
AGA: Appropriate for Gestational Age
BAER: Brainstem Auditory Evoked Response (aka: ABR)
BVM: Bag Valve Mask
CBC: Complete Blood Count
CMV: Cytomegalovirus
CNS: Central Nervous System
CPT: Chest Physiotherapy
CSF: Cerebrospinal Fluid
D/C: Discontinue (medication or treatment)
DNR: Do Not Resuscitate
ECG/EKG: Electrocardiogram
EEG: Electroencephalogram
GERD: Gastroesophageal Reflux Disease
HELLP Syndrome: Condition in pregnancy consisting of: Hemolytic anemia, Elevated Liver enzymes, and Low Platelet count
HIPAA: Health Insurance Portability and Accountability Act
IUGR: Intrauterine Growth Restricted
IVH: Intraventricular Hemorrhage
KUB: Kidney, Urinary, Bladder area for an X-ray
LBW: Low Birth Weight
MRSA: Methicillin Resistant Staphylococcus Aureus
NEC: Necrotizing Enterocolitis
NICU: Neonatal Intensive Care Unit
NPO: Non Per Os (Latin for Nothing by Mouth)
PDA: Patent Ductus Arteriosus
PRN: Pro Re Nata (Latin for According to Need)
PT: Physical Therapist/Therapy
PVL: Periventricular Leukomalacia
OT: Occupational Therapist
ROP: Retinopathy of Prematurity
RT: Respiratory Therapist
SCBU: Special Care Baby Unit (same as NICU, some hospitals may use this acronym)
SGA: Small for Gestational Age
TPN: Total Parenteral Nutrition
UA Line: Umbilical Arterial Line
UV Line: Umbilical Venous Line
VLBW: Very Low Birth Weight
VSD: Ventricular Septal Defect
WIC: Women, Infants, and Children

a b c d e f g h i j k l m n o p q r s t u v w x y z

DEFINITIONS

ABR/BAER (Auditory Brainstem Response/Brainstem Auditory Evoked Response):
This is a general hearing test administered to all the NICU babies usually at a certain gestational age and certainly before your baby leaves the hospital.

NICOLE'S TAKE:

When I first heard them talking about this test, I literally thought they were saying my son needed a bear. Was that like a teddy bear he required for emotional comfort?

Acidodic/Acidosis:
The level of acid (versus bases) in the blood. Doctors may stick your Preemie's heel to run levels on his blood and ensure that the oxygen and carbon dioxide levels are where they should be. If too much carbon dioxide builds up, your baby's blood will become acidodic. Acidosis is used to assess either respiratory acid-base status, the kidneys ability to excrete acid, or the effect of certain medications (such as diuretics) on acid-base balance. These may all be thrown off balance due to conditions such as **sepsis** in Preemies.

Albuterol:
Common lung treatment medication administered by a nebulizer (a device allowing the medication to be breathed in through the flow of air). The infant will either receive these treatments with a special attachment that fits over the mouth and nose or without the mask (referred to as "blow by"). This medication is often given to babies with **Bronchopulmonary Dysplasia (BPD)**.

Apgar Score:
Usually the first test your newborn receives, Apgar is a scoring method to help doctors and parents understand and evaluate the infant. Using a scale of 0 to 2, the baby's elements of respiration, color, heart rate, muscle tone, and response to touch are rated. A perfect score would be 10 (2 points on each element). This is a preliminary indication that, while meaningful in some contexts, cannot provide with any accuracy the course your baby will take in the NICU.

Apnea:
Simply put, when your baby stops breathing. In premature infants, the cessation of breathing is common, though no less scary. Thankfully, your baby is monitored. When he or she stops breathing for any period of time, the monitors by the isolette will alarm and the nurses will take

immediate action. Many Preemies return home with monitors for both apnea and **bradycardia** (low heart rate) episodes until the infant can fully breathe on their own. We know several, though not all, contributing factors to this condition.

Two of the most common types of apnea are **Central Sleep Apnea** and **Obstructive Sleep Apnea**.

Aquaform:
A preservative and unscented healing ointment used by pediatricians to protect the infant's delicate skin and help to soothe dry/irritated skin.

NICOLE'S TAKE:

Once during touch time, perhaps as compensation for living through unanswered questions, the nurse let me put on Nicholas's Aquaform to keep his skin moist (as if his 97% humidity isolette wouldn't do the job). Shivers went through me; I was struck by the aching brittleness of his bones beneath wet, crêpe paper thin skin.

Arterial Blood Gas:
*See **Blood Gas***

Arterial Line:
A catheter that is placed in an artery (rather than vein) to monitor **blood pressure** and draw blood. Potential complications with an arterial line include: blood loss, infection, clot, and loss of fingers, toes, hands/wrists, and/or feet.

Asphyxia:
Where breathing is reduced or stopped in some manner. Asphyxia implies an inability to meet the tissue oxygen needs of the body, which can lead to **acidosis**.

Aspiration:
The inhalation of non-gaseous matter into the lungs (food, liquid, refluxed material, etc.). These can land in the lungs and cause **pneumonia**.

Audiologist:
A medically-qualified specialist who is trained to work with and evaluate hearing loss. He or she will also help find solutions to hearing impediments, including fitting patients with aids and other devices.

Auxiliary Temperature:
Measuring the baby's temperature under the arm. These temperatures tend to run approximately 1 degree Centigrade below rectal temperature (the most accurate, taken through the buttocks), and are far more accurate than skin temperatures taken by leads (which tend to detach easily).

NICOLE'S TAKE:

When your infant gets home you might want to investigate, using a Thermostrip by Hallcrest on your baby's forehead, if she is running a temperature. They are incredibly accurate—I know because Nicholas wears one 24/7 due to his Disautonomia by Prematurity—He is unable to regulate many autonomic functions—one being his body temperature. But we found using a Thermostrip on his forehead, another in the bathtub, and another for his bottles gave us such a relief in knowing we could never end up with any kind of accidental burn. A Safety Thermostrip Thermal Pack is available at PreemieWorld.com.

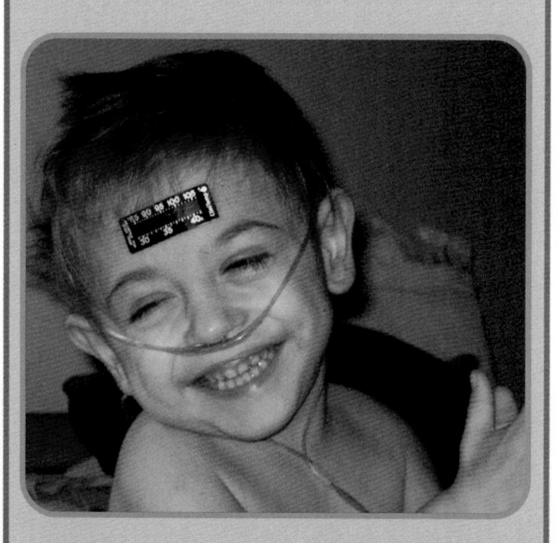

Nicholas is happy with his thermostrip
Photo Credit: Nicole Conn

Bagging:
Slang for respirating the infant with a BVM (Bag Valve Mask) or Ambu Bag, usually when changing over vent lines or in cases where the baby is not breathing on his or her own. This is very much like the resuscitation bag you will want to have in your home prep kit.

Bands:
A commonly-used term by doctors when talking about labs. Bands are immature white blood cells that are seen as part of a **CBC** (Complete Blood Count) and are noted in the differential or "diff." A spike in a band count ("bandemia") can indicate infection. The sicker an infant is, the more immature white cells/bands he or she will make to help his or her body fight infection. Remember not to get stuck on looking at simply the number of bands; they tend to mean a lot of things and most doctors only rarely get this detailed with a family.

Bilirubin/Bili Lights:
Bilirubin is the breakdown product made by the body from old red blood cells being removed from the circulation. Bilirubin is processed through the liver, but many premature infants' livers are too underdeveloped to process the by-product known as bilirubin from the blood. This leftover bilirubin accumulates and travels throughout

the body and turns the skin yellow (a condition known as **jaundice**). Bili lights are photo-therapy light sources which help to resolve this issue. Note the old Model-T goggles Becky wears to keep her eyes protected.

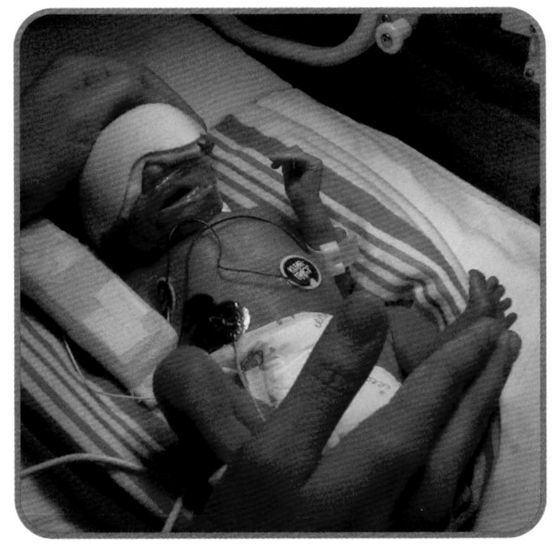

Becky under the lights
Photo Credit: Gregg Discenza

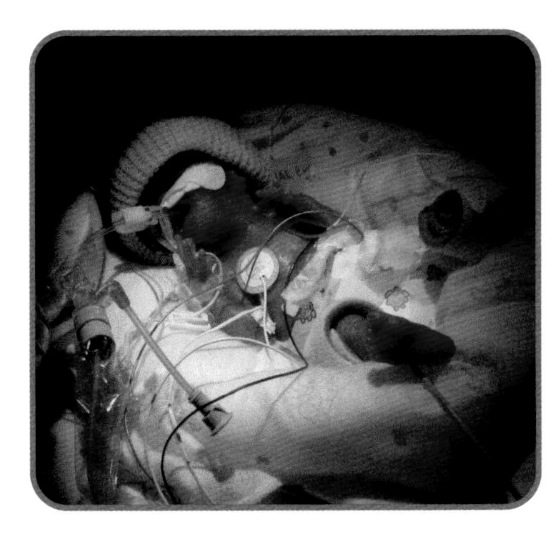

Nicholas under phototherapy day 2
Photo Credit: Brian Hoven

NICOLE'S TAKE:

Sometimes the stuff that looks the worst is the easiest on your baby.

A needle and catheter stick straight out of Nicholas's head—he looks like a little Frankenstein baby. But it's the best spot to get blood. The nurses praise his juicy veins. I know it looks much more awful than it is, but it still sends shivers up the back of my spine.

Blood Gas:
The way that physicians measure the amounts of oxygen, carbon dioxide, and acid in the blood. The results are used primarily to monitor respiratory support, often by pricking the fat pad on the side of your baby's heel for blood (known as a "heel stick"). Blood gases early in care are usually obtained through the umbilical catheters (*see* ***UA Line***).

!

Many NICUs haven't properly trained their staff and don't perform heel sticks correctly. They stick the heel itself rather than the fat pad along the inside of the heel. This is far more painful to the infant and could cause some long-term effects.

Nicholas's foot often looked like a swollen strawberry. Please request a different staff person poke your baby if you begin to notice this as a trend.

Blood Pressure:
The pressure of blood within the arteries. It is the measurement of the pressure needed by the heart to pump blood throughout the body. The pressures noted are: the systolic (the peak pressure during a heart contraction); the diastolic (a lower pressure noted during heart relaxation); and the mean (an average of the systolic and diastolic). The most important blood pressure is the mean, which should run abound 25-40 mm of mercury (Hg), depending on your baby's gestation and size. It may be even higher in the term infant.

Bolus:
A quantity of medicine or food that is ready for swallowing, usually delivered from the **G-Tube**.

Bonding:
It's easy to forget Parenting 101 when faced with the dire and emergent issues of the NICU, but what your baby needs most from you is for you to be a parent. Bond with your baby as much as humanly possible through touch, smell, sound, and the best ingredient of all—love.

Bradycardia (Brady):
When your baby's heart rate goes down below its normal range. You will usually hear the term "he's brady-ing" or "having bradys." This is a very common event in Preemies; however, there can be any number of causes, significant and insignificant. It can be something as natural as the baby trying to pass a stool, or simply experiencing reflux. Or it may be something more dangerous when the baby's heart rate is lower for more than 15 to 20 seconds.

Most hospitals have a general "brady" rule linked to Discharge Day (at Cedars, the infant had to be "brady-free" for 5 days" before getting off the monitors and going home), though this process will vary dramatically from one NICU to another.

Brain Bleed (IVH/Intraventricular Hemorrhage):
The blood vessels in your baby's brain are very friable and can bleed rather easily, even when the infant is moved gently in some cases. There are generally 4 levels of brain bleeds (from 1 to 4). Grade 4 is the most serious and can be the source of seizures, blindness, and severe retardation.

The doctors normally scan for brain bleeds within the first 24 hours

(the most critical), then after three days, and then after one week. The chances of a brain bleed occurring after one week are dramatically decreased. Often they will do a final brain bleed check at week six.

- What stage is my child's brain bleed?
- What can be done medically to help my child at this point?
- What can I do to help my child?
- What are the long-term outcomes for this stage of a brain bleed?
- Is there anything else I should know at this time?

NOTES:

____
____
____
____
____
____

It doesn't necessarily follow that long-term and/or severe damage occurs to an infant that experiences brain bleeds.

Breastfeeding:
Breast milk provided directly or through pumping, is one of the best medicines for your baby. It provides protection from all sorts of illnesses that cow-based formula can't, and helps in areas such as brain development and reducing infection. *Note:* Stress can affect production of breastmilk so if that happens, ask for help from the NICU's **Lactation Consultant.**

Reality of Preemie Breastfeeding

Breastfeeding can be challenging for preemies and moms. It can take time to master. Focus on the end goal, not the amount of time to that goal. And request the help of a seasoned NICU **Lactation Consultant** to help get you started. Be prepared for the lactation consultant or your nurses to touch your breasts as you attempt to get the baby to latch on. While odd, it is normal practice.

- Will I be able to breastfeed my Preemie?
- What if I have low milk flow?
- What if my baby won't latch on?

a b c d e f g h i j k l m n o p q r s t u v w x y z

- What do I do if my baby spits up after the feeding?
- What are the signs of a blocked duct and how do I handle that?
- If I am unable to provide breast milk, what are other options that will give my baby similar nutrients?
- Does this hospital carry 100% human milk-based products?

NOTES:

____

____

____

____

____

____

- AAP Breastfeeding Guidelines: ***https://preemie.us/HealthyChildrenHumanMilk***
- CDC Breastfeeding Page: ***https://www.cdc.gov/breastfeeding/index.html***
- WHO International: ***https://www.who.int/topics/breastfeeding/en/***
- EHMD Video: ***https://www.preemie.us/HealthyChildrenHumanMilk***

Pumping breast milk is another great way to help your baby, especially prior to attempting breastfeeding and beyond. Ask a Lactation Consultant to teach you how to use the breast pump in the hospital and, if possible, rent one. Hospital-grade pumps are the best though you might be able to find a portable breast pump that can work just as well on the road.

Bronchodilator:
A drug that relaxes the smooth muscle in the airways leading to the lungs and dilates airways to assist the breathing. This is used in the treatment of many Preemies, not only in the NICU but also post-Discharge Day for those with chronic lung disease and/or asthma. An inhaler and/or **nebulizer** help to maximize the treatment.

These drugs, unfortunately, tend to be grossly overused and rarely improve your baby's condition. Ask your physician why the bronchodilator is being used and what they hope to achieve with its use.

Bronchopulmonary Dysplasia (BPD; aka Chronic Lung Disease/ CLD):
A common problem in which the lungs have abnormal tissue development and lung development, Preemies are at

risk for this condition which develops over time due to extended use of the ventilator (as opposed to being a condition with which your baby was born) and exposure to oxygen. Infants with more severe BPD/CLD will be much more susceptible to respiratory illnesses, especially **RSV**. The good news: the larger your baby's lungs grow the less of a percentage of those lungs is damaged. Babies' lungs continue to grow and add new cells until about 8 years of age, and most children are left with no long-term residual. They can play and exercise normally in nearly all cases.

- What medications will my baby need to treat this?
- What are the side effects of the medications my baby will be taking?
- What types of precautions will we need to take upon discharge?
- What is the long-term prognosis for this matter?
- Is there anything else I should know about this matter and my baby's treatment and prognosis?

NOTES:

Bronchoscopy:
A procedure usually conducted by a **neonatologist**, thoracic surgeon, or **pulmonologist** wherein a scope views not only the patient's lungs but the trachea, vocal chords, voice box, and bronchi. This allows direct visualization of the airways of the lungs, if not the alveoli. However, biopsies are not possible with premature infant scopes.

Broviac/Broviac Catheter:
Very much like a **central line**, but made of a very soft material with a cuff on the end to keep the line inside the skin of the patient. These lines are burrowed into/under the skin and then enter the vein. The cuff is made of material which "scars" into the tissue around the entry site in hopes to keep the line in for as long as it is needed, occasionally for months (sometimes even years) in rare cases. The tip of the Broviac enters the large vessels near the heart, a necessity to provide IV medicines and nutrition.

Broviacs come in various sizes to fit Preemies. The downside to Broviacs, as with all central lines or any foreign materials that are placed within the skin and circulatory system, is a high risk of infection and chance of clots forming around the foreign material. This can enter the blood as well as at the entryway to the heart.

For more information on Broviacs, visit ***www.eapsa.org/parents/resources/catheter.cfm***.

Cardiologist:
Doctor specializing in the care of the heart.

Cardiopulmonary Resuscitation (CPR):
A set of chest compressions and breaths that can be used anywhere to revive a person that is not breathing or is breathing irregularly or shallowly. You will be required to take an Infant CPR Class prior to your baby's discharge from the NICU.

Cardiorespiratory Monitor:
*See **Monitors.***

Catheter:
Usually one thinks of this as being a tube for urination, but a catheter is any thin plastic tube that is flexible in nature and is used to deliver drugs, fluids, etc. through veins.

CC:
Abbreviation for a milliliter: one one-thousandth of a liter (33.814 US fluid ounces).

Central Line:
Similar to a **Broviac**, a central line winds its way from vein to end up in the right atrium of the heart. These lines are life-saving to the patient and often allow a Preemie to leave the hospital and receive much needed

NICOLE'S TAKE:

After Nicholas came home we simply could not keep weight on him. He went into severe failure to thrive. It was only after we took the extreme measure of putting in a **central line** that Nicholas really began to get better. He not only began to sit up, he started to crawl, soon walked and—well, thrived!

Never before had the need for good nutrition become so clear to me. But this too gave us a rollercoaster. While it was the miracle cure Nicholas needed, he also developed clots, had to go on blood thinners, and had far too many blood infections than we would have ever liked to imagine. Such is the nature of medicine!

medication, fluids, and or **TPN** in the comfort of his/her home.

Central Sleep Apnea:
A form of apnea caused by the brain's inability to keep breathing muscles working during sleep. Many short periods of apnea are normal in Preemies since their central nervous system is not fully developed; however, it can have serious implications if prolonged.

Cerebral Palsy (CP):
A muscle and coordination disorder caused by some form of neurological (brain) injury before, during, or after birth. There are several varieties of CP and many are not obvious for a number of years. While this diagnosis can be devastating, it is important to note that there is extensive research on prevention and management of this disorder. Many people go on to have very productive lives with CP.

An estimated 10-20% of Preemies born under 1000 grams at birth weight will develop CP.

However, babies born at less than 3.3 pounds (1510 grams) still have a higher risk of CP than babies that are carried full-term. Roughly 8 to 15% of the under-1500 gram Preemie population will develop some form of CP. These numbers are merely estimates as many children are not tracked after they leave the hospital. If you have any concerns about your infant, please contact your doctor.

- United Cerebral Palsy: ***www.ucp.org***
- *Cerebral Palsy: A Complete Guide for Caregiving* (Freeman Miller, M.D. and Steven J. Bachrach, M.D.)
- *Children with Cerebral Palsy: A Parents' Guide* (Elaine Geralis)

Chest Physiotherapy (CPT):
A form of **physical therapy** wherein the **respiratory therapist** or nurse will lightly tap upon the infant's lung area (front and back) to clear airways and loosen phlegm and congestion. Although this treatment can look alarmingly brutal, it actually gives most infants a sense of well-being. The rhythmic tapping of a rubber paddle to the chest is a remarkably effective and non-invasive therapy.

Chronic Lung Disease (CLD):
*See **Bronchopulmonary Dysplasia (BPD).***

a b c d e f g h i j k l m n o p q r s t u v w x y z

Chux:
A water-proof absorbent towelette made for incontinent older patients and used in the NICU for bed baths. Chux can also be used at home for home care.

DEB'S TAKE:

Chux are a huge help with a school-age child having a variety of illnesses. Don't just assume they are for the post-NICU period for home health care needs. So if you get some of these to take home—hold onto the extras in a clean place for years down the road and you'll thank me!

Coding/Code Blue:
Slang for when a baby is crashing and needs resuscitation to stabilize heart rate and breathing. Unfortunately, it comes with the territories of **Micro-Preemies**, who are too under-developed to handle the rigors of being outside of the womb.

Colostomy:
Very similar to an **ileostomy**, but instead of cutting into the small intestine, doctors cut into the large intestine and bring it through the abdominal wall to excrete waste. A plastic bag is attached externally to collect the waste material.

NICOLE'S TAKE:

Nurses push past us in rush. "There he goes again," I hear someone mutter.

When we round the corner into Bay 4, we see a team of doctors, nurses, and RTs standing at Nicholas's isolette.

He's coding. A rush of people is suddenly all over my son. I back into a wall, feel my feet sink beneath me. I realize I'm crying only when someone hands me a tissue. I can't breathe. I recognize the voice of another mother telling me I need to be strong. "Don't tell me what I need!" I want to scream, but I can't speak.

Then it happens: a calm runs through my entire center. I know he will be okay. Within moments, Dr. Chow comes to comfort me. "He's going to be alright."

That night I don't want to leave. I *cannot* leave, but at some point I have to see Gabrielle. She doesn't understand why her Mommy Co-Co has been gone so much.

A few days later, I return with my sister for touch time.

But there is no touching. Nicholas has coded again. And the fellow on service explains that the previous code wasn't a bad one. This

one is. I ask myself, is there such a thing as a good code?

This time, his heart has simply flat-lined. I sit there for hours, paralyzed. What have I done? What was I thinking? I stare at the little frog bird in the isolette. They're right. The honeymoon is over. And with it goes a little of the denial. He's so incredibly fragile.

They put him back on the oscillator jet vent. He remains unstable. And I feel like I suddenly understand what hell is.

Colostrum:
The yellow-ish breast milk that comes out after you start pumping breast milk or breastfeeding. It is also known as "Liquid Gold" by the nurses because it provides the much-needed fats, antibodies and nutrients for your baby.

Complete Blood Count (CBC):
A regularly performed test which informs the doctors of any potential issues that might be developing in the baby, often relating to anemia and infection. This test can also show low platelet counts, and it is not unusual for Preemies that are sick to not only get blood transfusions but also platelet transfusions.

Continuity of Care:
The concept that the same nurses will take care of your baby as often as possible. It is important to find the best **primary nurse** as well as a primary **neonatologist**. Every hospital assigns the nursing staff and continuity of care differently, but without a solid chain of medical information being transferred to the correct people, your baby's well-being can be in jeopardy. While it is not something that can be expected with all NICUs, ask if it is possible in yours.

DEB'S TAKE:

In my recovery room, I stared at the breast pump the morning after delivering Becky. Looking at my husband, I said we should consider my starting to use the pump since no one had come around to talk about pumping or breastfeeding in general.

I was disappointed with the tiny amount of yellow stuff that had come out after the 20 minutes of pumping. I told Gregg to take it to the nurse and see if we just needed to throw it out or not. Gregg left and came back with a big grin on his face. "It is perfect—the nurse was so excited and stated that it was Liquid Gold for Becky. She is rushing it down to the NICU right now."

The Gold Rush had nothing on how I felt at that moment. I felt like I had won the lottery and could finally do something to help my daughter.

a b c d e f g h i j k l m n o p q r s t u v w x y z

NICOLE'S TAKE:

I'm only ten days into this and I know what my biggest problem will be: Continuity of Care. Why in the hell can't we get the same nurse two days in a row?

I must have gone through every nurse in the planet…The common refrain to this demand is "Nursing Shortage."

With the global shortage and having so many registry nurses and staffing issues, how can one most effectively create a team?

This is why, if you find yourself involved in a long-term stay, it becomes imperative to have a parent play the "continuity role." When one's son is hanging by a thread it's hard enough. But when it's during a shift change it can be devastating—medicines get missed, change in dosing isn't indicated—nurses are in a rush to get out of the hospital after a long 12 hour shift on their feet. People make mistakes.

Ironically it was during a shift change that things actually changed for the better at times when Nicholas was very ill. A new approach can change a situation significantly.

But with a **Micro-Preemie** being challenged by a host of preemie complications, it's imperative to have a primary doctor who maintains a global overview of the plan of care.

Part of the job as the parent/advocate is to strive for a primary **neonatologist** to assist with the most complex situations your baby will face. It is important to remember that in a good NICU the physicians should be working together as a team. It's sometimes difficult for this to take place if doctors have conflicting views as to what's the best care for your baby, and that's why it is especially important for you to be involved as a critical member of the team. While continuity of care can be your biggest nightmare, when the team works together, in harmony, it is a thing of beauty.

Continuous Positive Airway Pressure (CPAP):
A mask with nasal prongs that fit into your baby's nostrils to aid breathing. The oxygen flows through the cannula with certain levels of pressure to help keep the lung sacs open. This is <u>not</u> the **ventilator** (which actually breathes for the baby); rather, it's a booster that helps the baby to breathe on its own. It is also often the next step in weaning an infant off the **ventilator**.

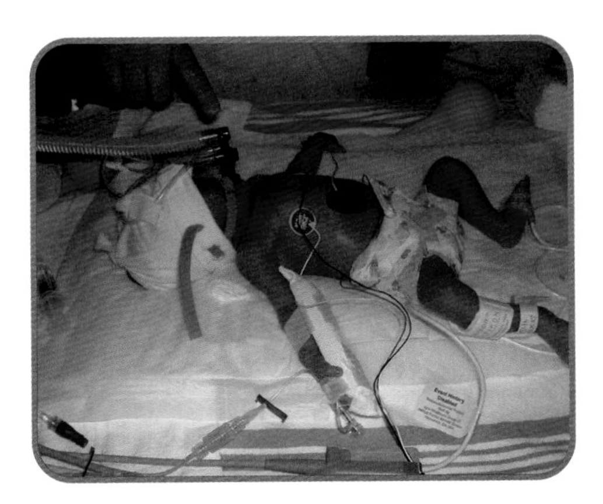

Becky on the CPAP
Photo Credit: Joseph H. Discenza

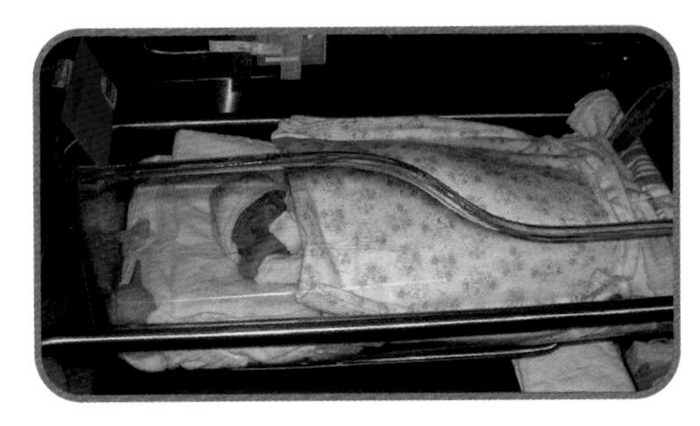

Becky's first day in a bassinet
Photo Credit: Deb Discenza

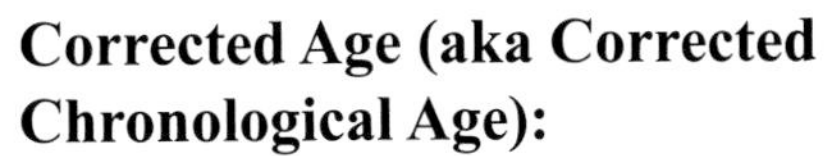

Corrected Age (aka Corrected Chronological Age):

The real time from the time a baby is born until now as opposed to the actual age from due date. If and when your baby doesn't hit the two month, four month, and six month milestones, subtract how many months premature they were born and then apply the appropriate developmental criteria.

Cribbed/Bassinet:

Slang for the time when a baby can be safely transferred from the **isolette** to an open-air crib. They usually do this by weaning slowly to make sure the baby does not get too cold or end up burning up too many calories keeping their body weight. This change means they can hold their body temperature and is a wonderful milestone to hit!

Remember that every baby is unique and what is normal for your infant may be far different than for another's. It is extremely difficult to hear that your toddler is developmentally delayed. Or brain damaged. Or mentally retarded. These terms cut parents off at the knees and are often only applied to a baby's progress in order to ensure services. When you go for assessments, try to prepare yourself to hear these terms—and see how it is you feel about them. But be careful how seriously you take them. A diagnosis—a label—does not make your child any less lovable and adorable. And even when you know your baby is delayed, as we certainly began to understand with Nicholas, there are always so many services available to help your baby to catch up.

Getting Cribbed:

When weaning, make sure temperatures don't cool dramatically at night!

Crit:
Slang for **hematocrit**, or the percentage of red blood cells. You will often hear a doctor or nurse say "We need to run a crit."

CT Scan/CAT Scan:
Acronym for Computerized Axial Tomography, an x-ray that puts together many x-rays to provide a three-dimensional picture of areas in the body, organs, structures, etc.

Cyanosis:
When the skin turns a bluish-gray or purplish-blue, indicating that there is insufficient oxygen in the blood. This observation is a critical one because it shows the baby is having problems breathing, or at least being able to produce enough oxygen for their organs.

Cytomegalovirus (CMV):
Many adults carry this virus, which includes a long-term fever and elements of hepatitis, in their blood. The issue for your baby is that so many adults carry the disease that if your baby is going to have a blood **transfusion** you need to make sure the blood is CMV negative. CMV can be easily passed onto the fetus causing hearing defects and hearing problems. It is the most common virus transmitted in pregnant women today.

NOTES:

DNR/Do Not Resuscitate:
Specific orders made by the parent to the professionals to not make an attempt to save the baby's life. *(See more about the emotional responses to DNR in the Self Care Section, pg 139.)*

NICOLE'S TAKE:

In my second week, the new neonatologist asks me, "While you're still dispassionate, when do you think you will put a DNR on your baby?" I looked at him dumbly and then through tears assured him I would never be dispassionate and the thought had not occurred to me.

But then it had to. I had to look at Nicholas from the point of view of the medical staff, who were all giving me clear signals that they didn't think he could make it with all the medical challenges he had, being born that early and that sick. It was a decision I wrestled with daily as I watched other parents put DNRs on their infants. I do not know how they actually arrive at that decision and wonder if I'm even capable of doing so.

Desaturation (Slang: Desat):
When your baby's oxygen levels in the blood go down. Oxygen levels need to be set and maintained very specifically for some infants as the oxygen and the force with which it is delivered can have severe ramifications. These ramifications include **brain bleeds** as well as the ever-present threat of **ROP (Retinopathy of Prematurity)**, in which too much oxygen gets to the eyes. This can cause vision damage or blindness.

Designated Donor:
A person, usually from your group of friends or family, assigned as the designated donor for your baby's blood supply in the case of blood **transfusions** or to have extra blood on hand during surgeries. It's important that the medical staff is aware that you have designated donors in the blood bank; if they are not, they will simply go to the general supply.

Developmental Delay:
Babies are expected to reach certain milestones (i.e. walking and talking) within a predictable amount of time. Preemies, due to their early birth and subsequent medical challenges, may take longer to reach those milestones. Many Preemies receive **occupational** and/or **physical therapy** to deal with all the various issues of being born too early: the stress it puts on the muscles, the stiffness in the bodies of infants that are on the vent for any length of time, etc. This therapy is very important for your baby. If

a b c d e f g h i j k l m n o p q r s t u v w x y z

your baby is vented, ask your nurse to get an **occupational therapist (OT)/ physical therapist (PT)** consultation. Some infants receive therapy early on after discharge, others do not require it and the parents can take a "wait and see" approach. Your pediatrician can guide you through this and may refer you to your area's **Early Intervention** program.

Discharge Summary:
A report that outlines the full medical history and current status of your baby, so that you will be able to provide your new pediatrician and any other specialists all relevant medical information. Presented on Discharge Day, it is also often used as a source document for medical and therapeutic services provided by the county and state.

Diuretic:
A drug that is used to help the kidneys release salt and water to drive urine production and increase urine output. Lungs of small preemies often have extra fluid that exacerbates breathing problems, and one way to rid the baby's lungs of fluid is to use a diuretic (the most common of which is Lasix). The side effect is that your baby can become "too dry" and lose too much fluid. It is very important to have your baby stay hydrated.

Ductus Arteriosus:
*See **PDA/Patent Ductus Arteriosus.***

Dump:
Slang for when an infant cannot handle the feeds. When feeds start coming out the rectum (or an ostomy bag if your Preemie has one) looking curdled and off-color, it usually means the baby is dumping or getting rid of the food without digesting it or absorbing its nutrients. This usually requires a change in formula and/or extra tests to see why the baby is not digesting properly.

Duo-Derm:
A thin layer of plastic to coat and protect the skin from **stoma** output, usually cut to shape and placed upon the skin over which the stoma bag is adhered.

Durable Medical Equipment (DME):
The medical equipment you may need to have at home prior to discharge of your baby. With Preemies it can include items such as oxygen tanks, **pulse oximeter** monitors for oxygen saturation, monitors for **apneas** and **bradycardia**, and feeding tube equipment. If your doctor prescribes any type of DME for home use, you will be trained by a professional on how to use the equipment.

DEB'S TAKE:

Becky came home on oxygen and an apnea monitor. I was scared to death that I was unable to medically care for her, but I swallowed hard and listened to EVERY word the DME trainer told me about the equipment and how to use it. Here I was thinking that post-NICU we'd be bringing home a baby, not all of these accessories.

My husband called me at work to let me know that the oxygen tanks had been delivered on time prior to Becky's discharge. I will never forget the word he used to describe the big tank in her room: "HUGE." I got home and stared at this pale green tank in my daughter's room, practically dwarfing everything else in there.

"Hey, that's cool," I noted, "Becky's tank kind of matches the décor."

Early Intervention:
A family-centered program, its therapists teach families how to help "exercise" their babies in order to stimulate them in areas of vision, speech, feeding, gross motor skills (walking, running), and fine motor skills (holding a crayon, self-care). While scheduling these sessions can be an overwhelming challenge, this much-needed therapy can make the difference in your baby's quality of life. If your baby needs some help in stimulating brain development to reach those milestones, EI is a great program.

Echocardiogram:
(**Abbrev: Echo**) A radiological scan of the heart. These are used to help identify **Patent Ductus Arteriosus (PDAs)** or other forms of heart disease. Many Preemies have little "holes" in their hearts that would have closed on their own (and usually do) prior to birth. Since they were born early, however, these are usually still open.

DEB'S TAKE:

Becky had been having some issues with the PDA not closing as well as some other defect issues, so they did an Echocardiogram on her right there at bedside. It was so bizarre to see my daughter's heart pumping away on a screen that was bigger than she was. But I was also heartened that they had all of this amazing technology to check these tiny babies.

Edema:
Swelling that can be an early sign of hypertension or **sepsis** in your baby. It can also indicate that your baby has too much fluid in their lungs.

Electrocardiogram (EKG/ECG):
A test which profiles the electrical impulses of the heart, taken in order to determine if the heart is functioning properly.

Electroencephalogram (EEG):
A test which profiles the electrical impulses of the brain. These tests are often run to show whether your baby has any signs of **seizure** activity. This is especially important in the event that your baby has had any **brain bleeds**.

Electrolytes:
The minerals and salts that control the fluid balance in the baby's body. It is absolutely imperative that the electrolytes are not out of whack as they are in charge of muscle contraction, the generation of the body's energy, and every biochemical reaction in the body. If your baby's electrolytes are out of balance, the doctors will order the necessary replacements of calcium, potassium, sodium bicarbonate, etc. These are commonly reviewed during rounds so that any necessary adjustments can be made on a daily basis.

Emesis:
Vomit.

Endotracheal Tube (ET Tube):
A small tube placed in your baby's windpipe to help with breathing.

Enteral:
By way of the bowel, as differentiated from parenteral, which refers to intravenous nutrition.

Extubation:
Extubation is one of your greatest milestones for you and your baby—that is if it's planned. Many of these babies routinely extubate themselves—accidentally. They pull out the tube—probably because it doesn't feel good in there. Sometimes they are actually ready to breathe on their own, and know better than we do that it's time. Other times they accidentally get their hands stuck in the way and fling it out because the tape on their faces has come loose.

Fellow:
Many NICUs and hospitals are teaching hospitals where interns, residents, and fellows learn their specialties. Fellows are training in a specific area of study (such as cardiology, pulmonology, or neonatology). They are doctors since they have completed medical school. By the way, a "fellow" may be a very experienced woman physician..

a b c d e f g h i j k l m n o p q r s t u v w x y z

Fine Motor Skills:
Movements in the small muscle groups of the body, including the hands, fingers, feet, lips, and tongue. Preemies may take longer than other babies (and require the aid of a **physical therapist**) to develop these skills.

Floppy Airway:
A "floppy" airway refers to one that has been stretched excessively, usually because the tiny infant needed a **ventilator** to support breathing for some time. The airway has lost some of its muscle support, which is temporary, but may take weeks or months from which to recover.

Floppy Tone:
A description applied to the lackluster tone of muscles in Preemies. For the most part this will turn into normal muscle mass, but for extremely premature babies this can sometimes be the first sign of cerebral palsy (a condition affecting roughly 10-20% of those born under 1000 grams).

Fontanel/Fontanelle:
The open or soft spot on the baby's head that will grow together. The concern with Preemies is that they are born so early that this soft spot is exposed for a greater length of time. Additionally your baby's head may often look very strange because of the lack of structure and definition.

Fortification:
Breast milk alone is insufficient for tiny preemies. Your team is likely to "fortify" your breast milk with extra nutrition.
Cow-based fortifier is commonly used but is not appropriate nutrition for your very low birthweight preemie. Human milk-based fortifier is a 100% human milk fortifier and the only one that exists for preemies under 1,250 grams. This fortifier is key to increasing calories, fats, minerals and the appropriate proteins so your preemie can safely grow. Human milk-based fortifier has been shown to reduce **Necrotizing Enterocolitis (NEC)** by as much as 77% and helps your baby avoid a lot of other problems like feeding intolerance, **Sepsis, Retinopathy of Prematurity (ROP), and Bronchopulmonary Dysplasia (BPD)**.

No Cow!
Credit: Bri Ziganti, Felice Media

a b c d e f g h i j k l m n o p q r s t u v w x y z

- What is my baby's current nutrition?
- Is my baby being fed my breast milk only?
- If not, is my baby receiving pasteurized human donor milk?
- Is anything else being added to my breast milk at this time or planned to be added in the future?

NOTES:

Fundoplication:
Surgery to correct extreme cases of **Gastroesophageal Reflux (aka GERD, Acid Reflux or Reflux)**, wherein a portion of the stomach is wrapped around the esophagus in order to stop contents from backing up to protect the baby's airway from aspiration.

Gastroenterologist:
A doctor who specializes in the area of the digestive system.

Gastroesophageal Reflux (aka GERD, Acid Reflux or Reflux):
Think spit up—a lot of it. Or think of a baby who may or may not spit up but is in a lot of pain and arching his or her back. This is the stomach "tie off" opening up and allowing the contents inside to go back up through the throat and out. This may require some tests, medication, and specific interventions after feedings, at naps, and bedtime.

Gastrostomy Tube/Button (G-Tube):
Placed in the stomach when your baby cannot learn to feed due to illness, being on the **ventilator**, etc. This is generally the best remedy for severe **GERD** or **reflux**. As their feedings increase, your baby will be pumped their allotment of food through a feeding bag that hangs from a medi-

cal ("tree") stand. It is run through a pump which delivers the dose of food at the rate that your infant can digest. This often happens during your stay at the NICU and continues after you bring your baby home.

Gavage:
The feeding of your baby through a tube into the stomach, either delivered through **G-tube** or **nasal gastric tube**.

- How serious is my baby's reflux?
- Are there tests that can check my baby's ability to swallow, empty, etc.?
- What types of medications will my baby require and for how long?
- What types of special home assistance should we consider to help our baby after Discharge Day?
- Are there special precautions I should take at home when putting my baby in the crib?
- Which specialist will manage my child's medication after discharge? Will we see a Gastroninterologist (GI) doc or can our pediatrician manage this?
- Is there anything else I should know about this matter?

NOTES:

DEB'S TAKE:

How are your washer and dryer doing? Time for replacements? Consider replacing them now instead of after your baby comes home (like I did). You'll thank me when you're not dragging tons of baby clothes down to the laundromat on a regular basis. And hey, maybe a large group of people you know would be willing go in on a set as a baby shower gift.

preemieworld

a b c d e f g h i j k l m n o p q r s t u v w x y z

Geneticist:
A doctor who specializes in genetics and heredity issues as well as syndromic issues. These may be the reason(s) that your baby is in the NICU. You'll see the geneticist on the NICU floor quite often because most infants with any sort of birth anomaly end up in the NICU and are assessed and then treated by geneticists along with the team.

Gestational Age:
The age as it relates to the 40 weeks of a pregnancy. In each month, week, and even day, very specific developments occur in your baby. When you know at what gestational age they are born, it will help you understand how developed (or under-developed) each of the baby's organs are and what issues he or she may face now and in the future. Always make sure you "adjust" for your child's age when looking at milestones across everything. You take the day that they were born (calendar age) and adjust for it based on their gestational age at birth. That will provide you with a sense of how "catch-up" is occurring.

Giraffe:
A type of **incubator** (the number of animal terms you'll hear may make you wonder if the "N" in NICU stands for "Noah's Ark").

NICOLE'S TAKE:

My son had one amazing geneticist who was truly giving and loving. Across the board, however, I would have to say that **geneticists** tend to be the most detached of the NICU specialists. Because they deal with genetic malfunction daily, many forget that the baby before them is the most loved and cherished soul his or her parents will ever meet. Try not to take it personally. It's not your fault.

DEB'S TAKE:

Who knew you had to do higher math when calculating your child's "adjusted" age? If you are worried about how your baby is doing milestone-wise always adjust and talk to your child's doctor.
.

Gram:
The metric unit of weight used in the hospital to weigh babies. 1000 grams equal a kilogram, which is roughly 2.25 pounds. And for you math geeks out there, with pocket calculators, 1 gram = 0.0022046 pounds.

HOW TO USE THE CONVERSION CHART:

1. Locate your baby's weight in grams.
2. Follow that column up to find your baby's weight in pounds.
3. Follow the gram weight to the left for the number of ounces.

Conversion Chart: Pounds + Ounces = Grams

OUNCES ∨ / POUNDS >	0	1	2	3	4	5	6	7	8	9	10
0	0	454	907	1361	1814	2268	2722	3175	3629	4082	4536
1	28	482	936	1389	1843	2296	2780	3203	3657	4111	4564
2	57	510	964	1417	1871	2325	2778	3232	3685	4139	4593
3	85	539	992	1446	1899	2353	2807	3260	3714	4167	4621
4	113	567	1021	1474	1928	2381	2835	3289	3742	4196	4649
5	142	595	1049	1503	1956	2410	2863	3317	3770	4224	4678
6	170	624	1077	1531	1984	2438	2892	3345	3799	4252	4706
7	198	652	1106	1559	2013	2466	2920	3374	3827	4281	4734
8	227	680	1134	1588	2041	2495	2948	3402	3856	4309	4763
9	255	709	1162	1616	2070	2523	2977	3430	3884	4337	4791
10	283	737	1191	1644	2098	2551	3005	3459	3912	4366	4819
11	312	765	1219	1673	2126	2580	3033	3487	3941	4394	4848
12	340	794	1247	1701	2155	2608	3062	3515	3969	4423	4876
13	369	822	1276	1729	2183	2637	3090	3544	3997	4451	4904
14	397	850	1304	1758	2211	2665	3118	3572	4026	4479	4933
15	425	879	1332	1786	2240	2693	3147	3600	4054	4508	4961

1 Locate your baby's weight in grams.

2 Follow that column up to find your baby's weight in pounds.

3 Follow the gram weight to the left for the number of ounces.

a b c d e f g h i j k l m n o p q r s t u v w x y z

preemieworld

a b c d e f g h i j k l m n o p q r s t u v w x y z

Weight

Weight is a significant factor in taking care of Preemies as both a sense of progress and a factor in medicating. You may hear the term "**dry weight**" being used during rounds. This is what the doctors consider to be the more accurate weight of your baby than what he may actually show on the scale, since many babies retain fluid during their illness.

Often you will see a grams-to-pounds conversion button on the scales they use to weigh your son or daughter. You can ask for them to push it so you can see where your baby is in pounds. You can also easily compute this number for yourself from the chart.

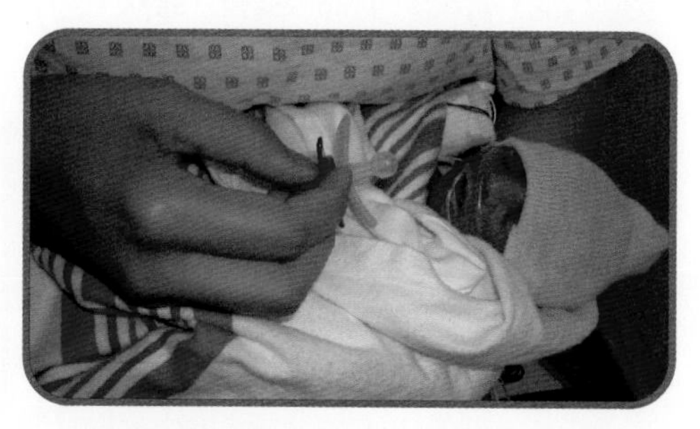

Tiny Becky in Mom's arms at last—be heavy, Becky!
Photo Credit: Robyn Kuniansky

Gross Motor Skills:
Movements in the large muscle groups of the body, including sitting, crawling, standing, and walking. Like **fine motor skills**, these are milestones for infants in general. However, Preemies may take longer (and require the aid of a **physical therapist**) to develop these skills.

Head Circumference:
The measurement taken with a small tape measure (usually paper) to determine the size of your baby's head. It's important to track these measurements on a regular basis—a small or large head size could be an indicator of a variety of conditions. Talk to your doctor about your baby's head circumference and see if there are any concerns so far.

Head Ultrasound:
A scan of your baby's head to determine issues such as **brain bleeds**. This type of scan may be performed several times during a NICU stay.

Hematocrit (HCT):
(**Slang: Crit**) Lab test to determine the percentage of red blood cells in your baby's blood. They may be anemic from loss of blood, malnutrition, or illness-destroying red blood cells.

Hernia:
Inguinal hernia is quite common for premature infants. For male babies

an opening exists in the abdominal cavity that is connected to the scrotum. Sometimes intestines slip through that opening. Normally this doesn't cause too much trouble unless the intestine swells up and blood cannot flow freely through it. Since the procedure to fix this is quite simple, doctors usually perform it before the hernia becomes a problem. This surgery is not very painful and the babies usually recover very quickly.

Hydrocephalus:
A condition of excess fluid in the brain. *See **VP Shunt**.*

- Hydrocephalus Association: ***www.hydroassoc.org***
- Hydrocephalus Foundation, Inc.: ***www.hydrocephaluskids.org/***

Hyperglycemia:
Condition in which there is too much sugar (glucose) in the blood.

Hypertonia:
High or tight muscle tone. It is quite common for infants on ventilators to exhibit tight muscle tone as it is very hard on their little bodies to be stuck in a certain position endlessly. If untreated, this can lead to dysfunction of the muscle or deformity. Ask your doctors or nurses for an **occupational/physical therapy** consultation.

Hypoglycemia:
Often referred to as "low blood sugar," a condition in which there is not enough sugar—which is critical for energy and stability in the body—in the blood.

Hypothermia:
When the body is too cold. This is dangerous: you don't want your baby's temperature to fall below 95° F (35° C).

Hypotonia:
Commonly referred to as "floppy," means low muscle tone. This may occasionally be a sign of early **cerebral palsy** and is treated with **physical therapy**. In many babies, however, it may only be a reflection of the fact that they are very ill and it will improve over time.

Hypoxia:
Inadequate levels of oxygen in the blood or tissues.

Iatrogenic:
A medical condition or problem that is actually caused by the doctor or the medical environment that is treating a patient.

preemieworld

NICOLE'S TAKE:

"You've heard of **iatrogenic** activity," Dr. Belagi suggests as he sits beside Nicholas, now comatose from having his **Broviac** pulled and enjoying a nice morphine snooze.

"Really Nicole, they've done many studies that show patients are much more likely to become sick when prolonging hospital stays."

"Yes, I remember you telling me that before."

"I think you need to get Nicholas home. I don't see what is keeping him here. He's up to full feeds, he's doing marvelously. I think you need to do this as soon as possible."

"Okay," I smile, not taking him seriously.

At 3:00 I prepare to feed Nicholas and when I pull his blanket back I see that he's soaked in blood. Earlier his Broviac had been pulled. I call for Belagi as I peel off his sopping T-shirt. Under the clear **Tegaderm** dressing is a huge quarter sized clot that looks like a miniature package of liver.

Belagi flies into action. Removing the dressing, he quietly asks the nurse and me to assist him. He quickly removes the dressing and huge clot and cleans the area. He asks me to put pressure on a four by four as he pulls off a huge swath of Tegaderm and covers half of Nicholas's body.

"He's lost a good twenty to twenty five cc's," Belagi holds up the crimson blanket, t-shirt, and clot. "We'll have to run a **crit** in a few hours."

KJ, one of Nicholas's primary nurses, returns a few minutes later and when Belagi shows the remains she shudders. "I've never seen anything like that. That thing is going to give me nightmares."

But there's more. When we go to change Nicholas's diapers he's still bleeding. We pull the dressing off again and apply a pressure dressing over a clotting Band-Aid.

"That's outta sight!" KJ proclaims.

"Now do you understand why I want to get you out of here?" Belagi says. "He needs to get out of this place."

I nod numbly. Yes, I finally understand the old phrase "the cure can kill the patient" and realize the hospital is becoming a danger to Nicholas.

So this was iatrogenic activity...

preemieworld

Ileostomy:
An opening in the small intestine from the outside of the body. Because this hole is where the baby's waste is being excreted, they have what is referred to an ileostomy or "**stoma**" bag attached at the opening so the fecal matter can be collected in the most sanitized manner possible. This hole is usually the result of an intestinal surgery and is most commonly necessitated by your Preemie having **NEC**. While the ileostomy is not exactly pleasant, the surgery that produced it is life saving.

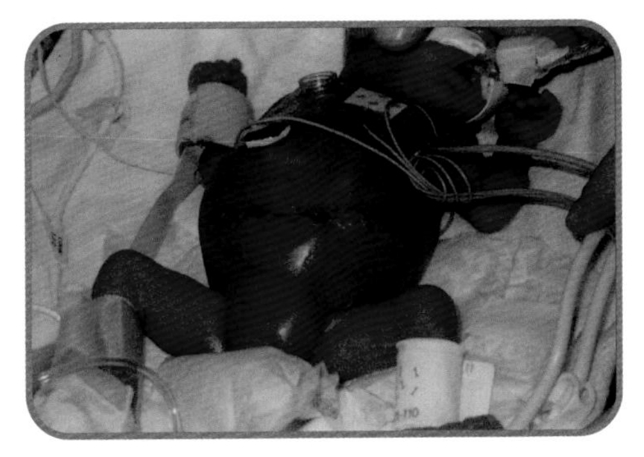

Nicholas's red cheerio stoma
Photo Credit: Brian Hoven

.

Illuminator:
The machine used to light up a baby's arms or legs to find the veins. Also known as a **trans-illuminator**.

Immune System:
This is your baby's natural way of fighting infection. If your baby is unable to fight an infection on his own, antibiotics will be prescribed.

NICOLE'S TAKE:

When I first see the "red cheerio" protruding from his tummy my first thought is that it looks nothing what I imagine intestinal material to look like—white bendy sausages. But then again, this is the inside flipped out and tacked down: a bird's eye view of the bowel, if you will.

Taking care of Nicholas's stoma bag becomes one of my biggest challenges. The acids from the ileum are devastating to his skin. I become OCD about it all and make the nurses crazy. But everyone that comes by says his skin is some of the best they have ever seen for having an ileostomy. Many of the nurses tell me they really haven't changed a stoma bag on a baby this small, so I'm happy to maintain the continuity of care on this one, even if the stink this "little man" can produce is eye-watering mind-numbing! Stephanie sucked out his mustard colored poo this morning (all 2 cc's of it). When she pressed the remaining air out of the bag, it was foul. Stephanie explained this part of the intestine produces the worst smell ever. She ain't kiddin'.

Incubator/ Isolette:
Informally referred to as the "baby cage," this is where your baby will live while in the NICU. While many infants can be seen, if your baby is born very early they will go "under cover." It is no substitute for the dark warmth of a womb, but it is imperative that the underdeveloped infants are shielded from the lights, sounds, and room air until they are ready. The isolettes are also temperature and humidity controlled. Arm holes provide access to touch your baby.

Indomethacin/Indocin:
Non-steroidal anti-inflammatory medication that is often used to help close the **Patent Ductus Arteriosus** opening.

Infusion Pump:
A pump used to deliver medicine over a specific period of time, whether it's a **G-tube** feeding of formula going into your baby's stomach, nasal tube, or an **IV** administering medication.

Intermittent Mandatory Ventilation (IMV):
*See **Ventilator.***

Intrauterine Growth Retardation (IUGR):
Condition in which the baby does not grow at the expected rate in the womb before birth. Babies in this situation can be premature or full-term but are significantly smaller in size and have a number of preemie-related health issues.

Intravenous Line (IV):
A tube inserted in your baby's arm or leg in order to give him medicine or fluids. These last only a few days and therefore need to be changed out. For long term use of this type of delivery of medication, fluids or parenteral feeds, the staff might insert a **Peripherally Inserted Central Catheter (PICC Line)**.

Intraventricular Hemorrhage:
*See **Brain Bleed.***

Intubation:
When your baby has a tube inserted into his throat and is put on the **ventilator**. Of all the contraptions in the hospital, this one is one of the most difficult to deal with: while it provides your baby with the ability to breathe, it is also the one thing that keeps you from seeing your baby's beautiful face. Additionally it can, at times, be terribly painful for both the infant and parent. Many hospitals have a standard practice of managing this pain by keeping the vented infants on low doses of pain medication.

Intubation also comes with inherent risks. First and foremost, a foreign body is in your baby's lungs. This increases the chance of infection.

Moreover, when infants begin to wriggle around they can accidentally **extubate** themselves.

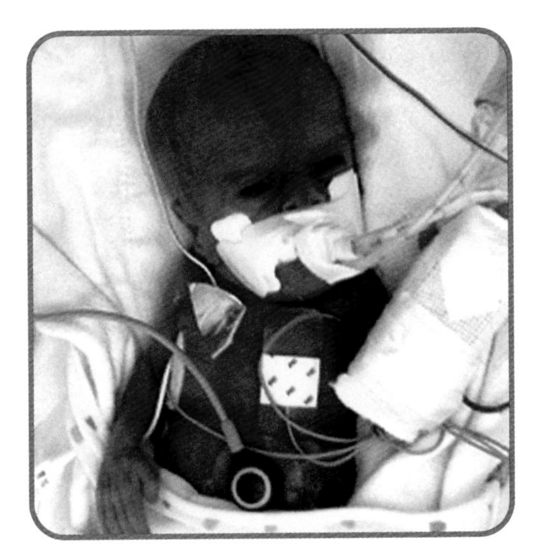

Nicholas intubated
Photo Credit: Brian Hoven

Jaundice:
A yellow discoloring of the skin due to immature livers having too much of a substance called **bilirubin** in the blood. This is a common diagnosis in Preemies. To combat this, your baby will undergo **phototherapy**.

Jejunostomy:
The jejunum is found in the middle section of the small intestine. A feeding tube is inserted in this section of the intestines bypassing the stomach altogether because there are medical reasons your baby cannot digest food in the stomach. Nowadays, this is rarely performed.

- What types of complications can I expect with my baby in the NICU?
- What types of complications can I expect with my baby at home?
- What are the long-term outcomes of the size and gestation of my baby?
- How can I help my baby thrive?

NOTES:

DEB'S TAKE:

Becky spent a lot of time under the "lights" and even had some extra time during Hurricane Isabel as it roared through the area. As the storm hammered down we joked that at least Becky was "kicking back at the beach and getting a sun tan." We had to make fun of the situation, because otherwise we would have fallen apart. It was just too much to comprehend on a serious level.

a b c d e f g h i j k l m n o p q r s t u v w x y z

preemieworld

a b c d e f g h i j k l m n o p q r s t u v w x y z

Kangaroo Care:
A wonderful way to connect with your baby and give him or her the amazing comfort and stability of health. This procedure involves placing your diaper-only baby (plus leads, etc.) on your chest. Your baby hears your heart beat and feels your body temperature. Quickly you notice that the monitor shows your baby's stats improving and that your baby is much more peaceful and can fall into a very deep slumber. This is something that both moms and dads can do (though dads need to be prepared for a little chest hair pulling).

One thing that's difficult sometimes in this high-tech world in which we live is to begin to rely more on the monitors and machines than the mother. This is where the natural course of mothering turns out, indeed, to be the best medicine.

If your baby is not strung up to a **ventilator** or in a medically fragile state, it probably won't be too difficult to get the staff to agree to have you kangaroo your baby. Dads too should join in the fun as soon and as often as they can.

If your baby is on a vent and/or fragile, getting to hold him or her can be another matter entirely. You may find nurses disinclined to pull out all the bells and whistles necessary to kangaroo your baby. It may be as simple as your baby being too ill. But it also requires the assistance of a **respiratory therapist** if your baby is vented and sometimes another nurse depending on how much

Kangaroo Care

The obvious origin of this word is from the manner in which a mother kangaroo holds her little joey snug in her pouch, keeping her baby warm and safe. But the concept of kangaroo care actually came from one of those necessity-being-the-mother-of-invention discoveries:

A doctor in Bogotá, Columbia didn't have the high-tech equipment of an isolette in which to place premature babies. The neonatologist decided to use the old and time honored tradition of using one body to warm another. They would place the newborn Preemies between the mothers breasts and bind the babies to their mothers, wrapping them up, safe and sound. The babies would stay there constantly, shifting position to breastfeed. Even if they happened to be on oxygen and any other monitoring the doctors might have available to them, the babies stayed snuggled in the bosom of natural care. They quickly discovered these babies did far better than babies that didn't have this advantage.

your baby is monitor dependent—how much stuff there is to move and re-arrange. Some hospitals may have a policy that kangarooing is not allowed while your baby is still on the vent for fear of **extubation**. Other hospitals are willing to make this exception and if they do you should take full advantage of this.

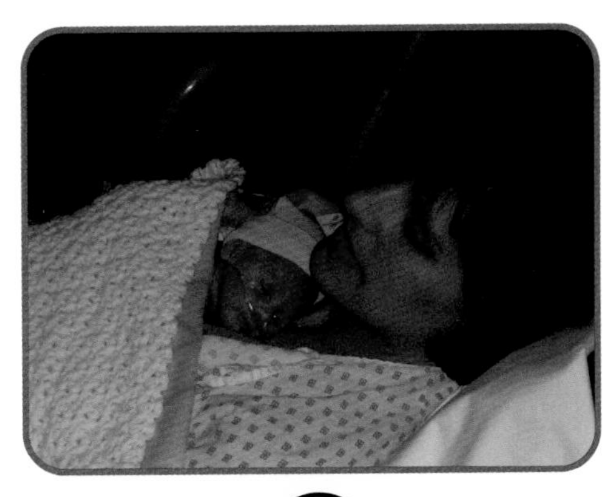

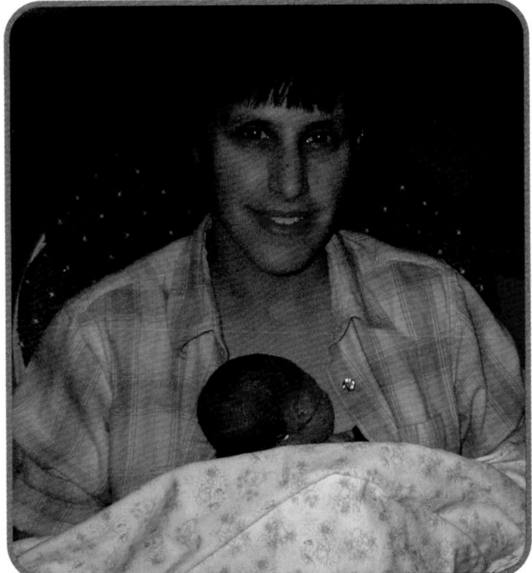

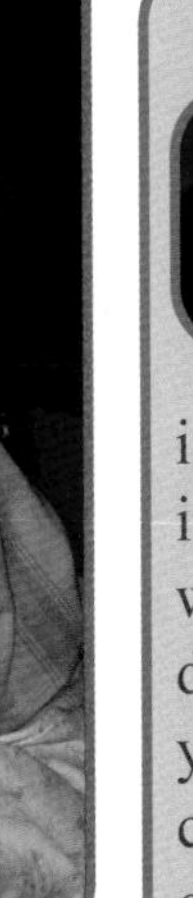

Deb kangaroo'ing Becky
Photo Credit: Gregg Discenza

NICOLE'S TAKE:

It can feel a little intimidating—downright horrifying—to think of holding your baby while she's strapped up to fourteen different machines. And I will tell you there were moments where I became very concerned that I was not doing something right. You literally feel as if you will break your own baby. Other moments where Nicholas started off well enough and suddenly began to have too many **bradycardias**—and his oxygen levels would dip below a safe level. There were times ten minutes into a **kangaroo** session that the nurses would have to take Nicholas back and return him to the safety of the **isolette**. I would feel such absolute pain and guilt in those moments. Had I hurt him? Had my selfish need to hold him done him harm?

Don't forget, Preemies turn on a dime. Your baby may start out okay while you are holding her and suddenly begin to show signs that she's getting sick. It happens and you need to remember every second you get to hold your baby you are doing her the best service you can. In the meantime you are also taking care of a core maternal need: holding your baby. It's as natural as it gets.

NICOLE'S TAKE:

Be persistent when you can. I was lucky. Most nurses will be happy to help you, but you will have those on occasion who resist having to go through all the work to hook up you and your baby. And oftentimes it is nothing more than the fact that they are very busy.

Remember: assisting you with **kangaroo care** is part of their job. When I began to have problems with a nurse who was being less than eager to help me, I got tricky. Most doctors absolutely believe in the advantages of kangaroo care. I had the doctor write in the orders that I was to kangaroo my son daily when he was well enough.

Why Kangaroo Care is Important for Mom and Baby:

- Babies gain more weight (they don't have to expend calories keeping warm)
- Babies' heart rates stabilize
- Babies have fewer episodes of **apnea**
- More natural than **isolette** for baby and mom
- Babies sleep and breathe better
- Babies maintain temperature better
- Babies are better able to learn to **breastfeed**
- Moms have less difficulty with breastfeeding
- Parents get to be parents
- Helps to heal the pain of separation
- Gives an opportunity for parent and baby to bond
- Babies are happier and cry less
- Helps parent to feel more confident and less helpless
- Parents see their infant as less of a "science project" and more of a baby

- When can I start doing Kangaroo Care?
- How long can each session be?

- How much notice do I need to give beforehand?
- Is there anything I need to prepare (i.e. not use perfumes, face makeup, body powder, etc.)?

NOTES:

____

____

____

____

____

____

Remember to bring a small pocket mirror with you on a **Kangaroo Care** day. That way you can get a chance to watch your baby without having to strain your neck. If you don't have a mirror, take a picture with your digital camera and look at the screen. A Kangarooed Preemie is a real joy to behold.

Kernicterus:
A condition in which the brain becomes damaged because your baby has an extremely high level of **bilirubin**.

Lactation Consultant:
A specialist who can help you with **breastfeeding** issues.

NICOLE'S TAKE:

One night I turned to see this couple that would visit every night at the same time. He was a rock star with long stringy hair and tall skinny build. She was a writer. They had adopted a 2 ½ pound Preemie, a baby girl.

Every night the new mom would take out knitting and the nurse would settle the wriggly little baby on dad's chest. She would sweetly drape a blanket over them, but not so much that the mother couldn't see. Atop the little girl's head propped one of the knitted caps the mom had made for her new daughter. It was one of the most blessed moments of peace I had ever seen. Dad would usually hum a sweet lullaby to her as he rocked his daughter to sleep. Mom would knit and soon Dad would be asleep, too.

Level I, II, III, and IV NICU:
*See **NICU.***

Licensed Practical Nurse/LPN (aka Licensed Vocational Nurse LVN):
More or less the same nursing level, you will not see many LPN/LVN nurses in the critical care levels

of the NICU. These nurses may help with your baby when he or she is getting closer to Discharge Day, changing wound dressing, monitoring the ins/outs and vital signs, etc. This level of nursing may figure heavily, however, if you have home health nurses that provide care to your baby post-discharge.

Liquid Ventilation:
A process wherein breathing more closely resembles true in-utero breathing for baby by having liquid be a part of the process. The vent fills the baby's lungs with a pre-calculated amount of liquid and then extracts an exact amount when breathing out that is required by an individual infant. (*See **Ventilator***). Oxygen is added to the liquid and carbon dioxide is removed with each breath.

Massage:
We bet you could use one right about now! And did you know that your Preemie could benefit from massage as well? Massage can relax your baby and help with sleep, development, and more.

Medicaid:
State medical insurance assistance for families without health insurance and based on poverty level. Check into resources at https://www.cms.gov and talk to your Social Worker for more information. Eligibility and services can vary by state.

- Does this NICU allow for baby massage?
- If so, is there a particular stage when this is encouraged?
- Do you have a staff member that can teach me how to massage my infant?

NOTES:

- Infant Massage USA: ***www.infantmassageusa.org***
- Loving Touch: ***www.lovingtouch.com***

DEB'S TAKE:

I loved giving Becky massages and had my first hint of the benefits as the NICU Nurse helped me give her the first bath. I lightly rubbed Becky's back with soap and she responded well. So after she came home I gave her baths regularly and did lots of gentle massage. It was so much fun—and I really feel it did a lot to help her with her feeding issues, weight gain, development gains and more.

Meningitis:
A very serious infection that is caused by inflammation to the membranes that surround the brain and spinal cord. This infection can be caused by many kinds of bacteria and/or viruses. It often appears very suddenly and can include high fevers, stiff neck, and vomiting. Since the Preemie cannot alert you to these symptoms they are often subjected to **spinal taps** to make sure there is no infection brewing. This procedure is necessary because meningitis can be fatal if not treated properly and quickly

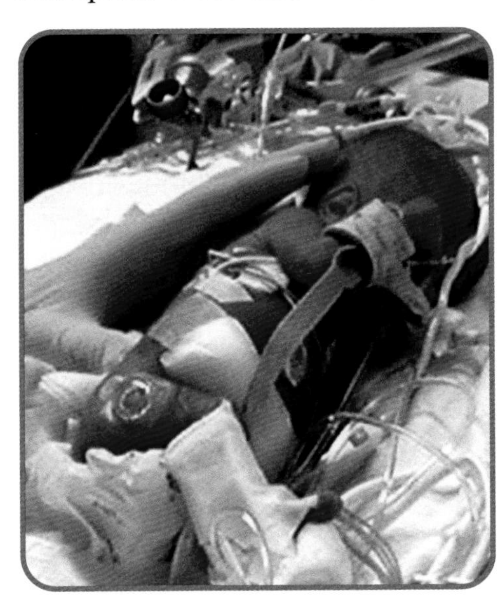

Nicholas prepped for spinal tap
Photo Credit: Nicole Conn

- What treatment is being provided for my baby?
- What can I do to help my baby at this time?
- What do you believe is the long-term prognosis for my baby?
- Are there any side effects from this treatment?
- Will any follow-up be needed because of this treatment?

NOTES:

Methicillin Resistant Staphylococcus Aureus (MRSA):
An infection that is resistant to a number of antibiotics and occurs most frequently in hospitals or other healthcare facilities to persons with a low **immune system**.

Micro-Preemie:
*See **Premature Infant**.*

NICOLE'S TAKE:

Here's the sweet irony of my Little Man: all my life I've been a miniatures freak. My family gifts me mini-typewriters, director's chairs, baby shoes. I even joked one day with my partner that I was too impatient for the entire gestational process. "Wouldn't it be cool if babies were born like after twenty weeks and you could just hold them in your palm? Put on little play diapers?" But destiny topped even my freakish imagination when Nicholas was born at twenty-five weeks. Be careful what you wish for!

Minimum Stimulation:
Minimal contact with the infant, including no touch, light, or sounds. Your baby is covered for hours at a time protected from natural light in order to simulate a darkened womb. *(See page 103 in NICU.)* Yes, parents are agonized by the concept of minimum stimulation, but it truly is the only way for baby to grow strong and to have as few developmental issues as possible along the way.

Monitor:
A machine that observes and explains everything that's happening to your baby with varying alarms/beeps to alert the staff on the status of your baby's well-being.

Monitor, Main:
This monitor will give you the basics: heart rate and pulse, **respirations**, **oxygenation**, and, on rare occasions, the level of carbon dioxide in your baby.

Myopia:
Ophthalmological (or related to the eye) term for nearsightedness. This is important for you if your baby undergoes **Retinopathy of Prematurity (ROP)**, for many of these babies who endure the laser surgery to correct or reverse ROP suffer from myopia. Often this condition reverses as the infant grows from toddlerhood to childhood. But others (like Nicholas) receive laser surgery and end up with thick coke-bottle glasses so they can adjust to their myopia.

Nasal Cannula:
If your baby is on oxygen, you will see a device with prongs that go up

his nose to deliver the much needed oxygen. The rest of the device is often taped to your baby's face with medical-type tape or special nasal cannula circular "Band-Aids" that are meant specifically for this use.

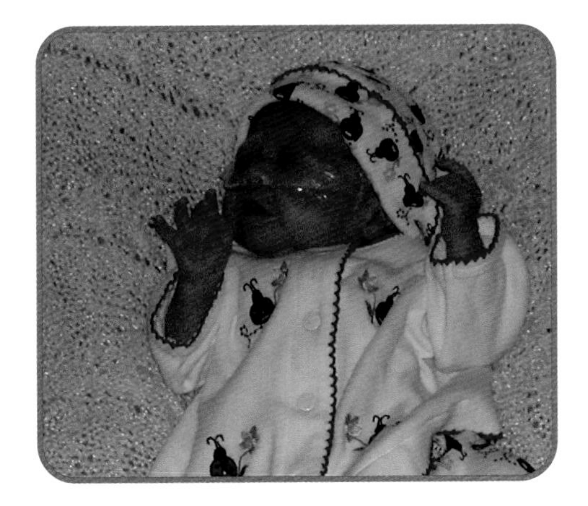

Becky with nasal cannula
Photo Credit: Deb Discenza

DEB'S TAKE:

When we brought Becky home on oxygen, we were given a roll of tape to attach the device to her cheeks. She developed a rash on each cheek, so we contacted the oxygen vendor and asked if they had something else we could use that would avoid the rash. They brought out dot-like Band-Aids and everything changed dramatically. Plus, our daughter didn't look like a poorly wrapped present. Ask your nurse or doctor about these dots!

Nasogastric Tube (NGT):
Made of soft plastic so that it doesn't hurt the baby, a tube that goes through the nose and passes through the esophagus into the stomach. The NG tube is used to take things out of the stomach and deliver food and medicine into the stomach. It is also used to check residuals. While it's not the greatest thing to look at and a bit discomfiting to the infant, they quickly become used to it and it's very helpful in keeping your baby well nourished and hydrated.

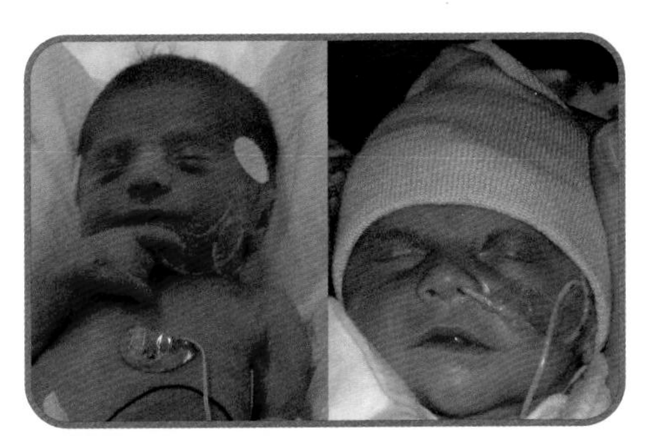

Becky with oral (left) and nasal (right) feeding tubes
Photo Credit: Deb Discenza

Nebulizer:
Also known as an atomizer, a machine that is used to blow mist and often medications (usually steroids or **Albuterol**) directly at the nasal passages. This is used to help support the lungs and help to open up the airways.

a b c d e f g h i j k l m **n** o p q r s t u v w x y z

Necrotizing Enterocolitis (NEC): A disease that primarily infects the immature bowel of the premature infant. Intestines are perhaps the weakest in the body's systems and are easily affected by infection and blood flow changes. NEC is a toxic inflammation in the intestine that literally kills the intestine.

Your baby's medical team knows that it is so very important to watch for this and to catch it immediately since it can spread so quickly and cause significant and quite serious damage. Often, NEC is caught by the signs of **sepsis** in the blood stream.

The least invasive measure of treatment is to have your infant be treated with a series of antibiotics while remaining off foods and being fed through a central line or **Broviac**. In the worst case scenario your baby will be subjected to surgery where the sick part of the intestine is removed.

- NEC affects 1-5% in 2-4000 births, but is the most serious as well as most common GI issues preemies face.
- Most babies who develop NEC will do so between the first 14 and 20 days.
- Of babies born weighing less than 1500 grams (3 lbs, 5 oz) about 10% will end up with some level of NEC.

Prior to a Diagnosis:

- What is the possibility of my baby getting NEC?
- What signs can I look for in my baby as I sit bedside and alert the nurses?
- What are good signs for me to keep in mind while bedside?

NOTES:

As A Diagnosis Occurs:

- What type of care is my baby receiving?

- What can I do to help my baby?
- Is surgery needed at this point?
- At what point may feedings occur again?
- What will be required for home-care?

NOTES:

____

____

____

____

____

____

____

Neonatal Intensive Care Unit (NICU) (aka Special Care Baby Unit/SCBU):
Area of the hospital in which your Preemie will be staying until Discharge Day. Levels of care are distinguished by specialty. All hospitals have variations on their NICU classifications, but generally they fall in one of three "level" categories.

- **Level I:** Support fairly uncomplicated late pre-term births from 35 weeks and up.
- **Level II:** Support births from 32 weeks up. This Hospital will often have a neonatologist on staff and a nursery devoted to NICU infants.
- **Level III:** Supports births below 32 weeks and under 1,500 grams that may require surgery.
- **Level IV, Regional:** Highest level NICU for a region that cares for the sickest of preemies that may require specialty surgery.

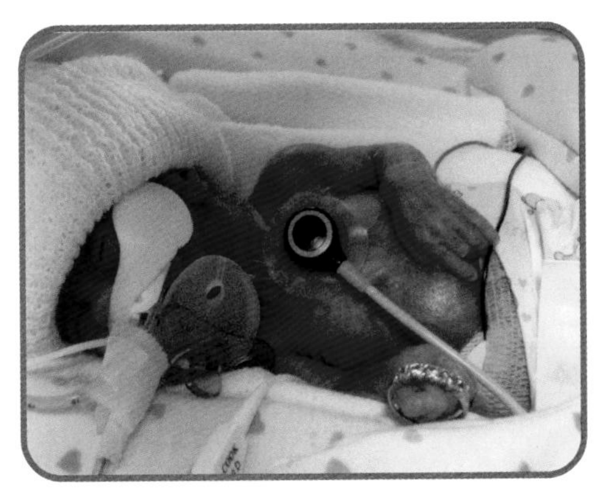

Nicholas holds Mommy CoCo's ring.
Photo Credit: Nicole Conn

Neonatal Nurse Practitioner (NNP):
Highly trained and skilled nurses with master's degrees (or higher). They are able to write prescriptions, order tests, interpret lab values, and generally make the plan of care for each infant under their own supervision.

Neonate:
A newborn infant.

Neonatologist:
Highly trained physician that specializes in the birth and care of premature and critically ill newborns and infants.

preemieworld

Neurologist:
Doctor that specializes and treats the nervous system. He or she will often be called in to assess your baby in the event there is any suspicion of **seizures** or the like.

NICU Psychosis:
A term the nurses and staff use for parents who have eroded under the stress of being in the NICU for too long—generally a mixture of loathing the NICU but being too afraid to leave it. (*See **NICU Psychosis**, page 159.*)

NICOLE'S TAKE:

From Nicole's Journal: It's one craaaaaaazy day. Bed 1: Sara's husband is visiting their daughter and the entire group of doctors are rounding with a large group of ten or eleven residents, fellows, nurses, and a caseworker. Bed 2: Holds one of the largest kids I've ever seen. Diabetic. He wails endlessly. Piercing. The new mom comes back and forth to breastfeed while her husband takes photos. And then Grandma and Great Grandma have joined in the general pandemonium. Bed 3: Is empty, thank God. Bed 4: Belongs to us, of course. My son is getting prepped for an eye exam. My nurse is very sweet, but young and seems a bit frazzled. She keeps trying to reschedule because Nicholas is running a fever.

Oh, my God—give the baby In Bed 2 some meds! He's squalling now. Bed 5 is a brand new mom with a new admission. Bed 6 is the newest little NICU baby at 665 grams and the Russian mom and family are up and down from her labor and delivery room. Bed 7 has been here three days and each day the mother brings in an entirely new contingent with her, some Hollywood elite—she's always on her cell phone (which we're not allowed to use but she snaps her fingers as if *"don't even go there"*).—Oh, and hey, some more visitors for the screamer baby. Bed 8 has the baby wired up to something that looks like the inside of an airplane cockpit—I will later discover it is an **EEG** machine to record **seizures**.

And now they've called the radiologist to do Nicholas's **EKG** that was scheduled for yesterday. And the people just keep coming. Doctors, rotating visitors (only two allowed isolette-side at a time) And more a'comin'. Tests. And people. And alarms going off. And leads falling off. And Nicholas pulling off his nasal cannula.

Suddenly I realize the woman right across from me is sobbing. She's got a cute Preemie, not intubated, but definitely small and pink and wriggly.

I'm assuming she's hormonal. She keeps crying. And crying. The huge baby next to me is screaming again and its almost shift change. I've already got a mega headache and Nicholas has just been assigned a nurse I've never seen before at shift change. She's just finished her training she tells me cheerfully. She's cute and utterly five years old. While I'm flipping out over this neophyte watching over my son tonight, I see the 665 grammer is going into distress. Heart rate is falling. I see it on the monitor and soon the isolette is surrounded by scrubs.

The mother of Bed 5's baby vomits all over, twice, and she loses it. Continues sobbing as two nurses try to help her. She is sobbing so loud now I'm wondering where her husband is—her mother—anyone. Someone help her. Too many realities are playing out simultaneously. Happy visitors with brand new healthy babies and a terrible drama is unfolding with the 665 grammer. I want to leave. Leave this insane asylum. I've way over had my fill of the hospital today and I now watch the drama unfold on the 665 grammer who for the next hour and a half will be endlessly poked and poked some more. Rotating needles as this poor baby's nurses diligently attempt to poke a vein.

It's time to poke Nicholas for his labs. It makes me feel guilty to ask my new little nurse to get an experienced vein poker to do Nicholas's presurgical IV. "I'll take a good look before I go get someone," she responds with the same cheery smile.

Oh, no you won't, I want to say. *You've never had my son before. You know nothing about him. You're five years old and have no experience—You and your cheeriness in the face of the grim realities of this bay. I know this is your newbie training. Cheerful, and please the mom. Especially this mom, I'm sure you've been told. Especially this mom who's on her way out with severe NICU psychosis.*

Normal Saline:
A form of salt water used for rehydration. The saline solution is roughly equivalent to the levels of salt in our own body. You might hear the staff refer to a "bullet" of saline—because of the small plastic bullet like shape that saline often comes in for things like helping with suctioning, cleansing areas of the body, etc.

Nosocomial Infections:
An infection that originates from the hospital. *See **iatrogenic***.

Not Impressed:
A common slang response from doctors and nurses to the results of a test.

preemieworld

This means they don't see anything that's impressed them into being overly concerned or to worry about.

NPO:
Acronym indicating no food or water for your baby. NPO is Latin for Nil per o (nothing by mouth).

Obstructive Sleep Apnea:
When the baby stops breathing during sleep because an actual obstruction stops oxygen from getting through. Often this problem is the result of the throat closing down or collapsing, which causes the infant to gasp for air. If this happens throughout the night, the infant may be difficult to arouse from sleep, since they are essentially not getting a good night's rest.

Occupational Therapist (OT):
A specialist trained to deal with the myriad stages of development from a muscular and neurological standpoint. They will also analyze the effects of being born prematurely on the development of your baby's **gross and fine motor skills**.

This therapy is very important for your baby. If your baby has been put on a **ventilator**, make sure you ask your nurse to get an **OT/PT** consult.

DEB'S TAKE:

One day my husband and I walked into the NICU to find our daughter in the arms of a woman who appeared to be stretching our tiny baby's arms and legs. "Hi, I am Theresa and I am Becky's **occupational therapist**," she said as she continued her work. My husband, ever the comedian, joked, "Occupational therapist? So what is Becky's job?" "To grow!" smiled Theresa. We all had a good laugh and have been good friends with Theresa ever since.

- At this time, how is my child's muscle tone?
- At this time, is there anything that concerns you about my child's overall development?
- Is there anything that I can do to help my child's needs in this area?
- Is there anything else I should know at this point or in the future to help my baby's development?

NOTES:

Oral Defensiveness:
A common issue for Preemies—especially for those who have been on a **ventilator**. Many infants have difficulty co-coordinating the **suck-swallow rhythm** in order to eat properly, though the use of their muscles in and around their mouths can be corrected with an **occupational therapist**.

> Preemies that have been on a **ventilator** have the additional issue of the gag reflex becoming extreme. Think of the poor infants who have lived with a tube shoved down their throat. Anything that triggers the memory of that feeling (e.g.: a piece of food passing through their mouth) will more than likely cause a gag reflex for them when first eating. Be patient. This will pass, but your baby may not enjoy the singular pleasure of eating until they can overcome a sense of danger from the food passing through their mouths and down their throats.

Over-Stimulation:
Your baby can get easily overwhelmed, even by you if they are having a tough day. Just as you are having problems adjusting to the lights, noise, chaos, and stresses of the NICU, your baby doesn't have your coping skills. One of the big signs of over stimulation is when your baby will put up one or more of his hands in a "stop" position. If so give him room to rest and not be so stressed. (*See* ***Minimum Stimulation***).

Oxygenation:
Adding oxygen to the body, such as through a hood, **nasal cannula**, **CPAP**, or a **ventilator**.

Oxygen Hood:
A hood made of plastic that covers your baby's head and has a tube attached that pumps oxygen to your baby. These are often used instead of **nasal cannulas** for periods of time to avoid tape on the face.

Oxygen Saturation:
The level of oxygen your baby is able to sustain in their blood. This vital percentage should be kept between 88% and 95% (never above 95%). This number is usually on the **main monitor** so that you can make sure your baby is doing well.

Parenteral:
The delivery of medication or nutrition in some manner other than the intestine. It may be by injection, perhaps subcutaneously, (under the skin), intravenous, intramuscular, (into the

muscle) as opposed to enteral. When you hear the term Parenteral Nutrition it is food being delivered via **IV**.

Patent Ductus Arteriosus (PDA): A common heart defect found in Preemies. The ductus arteriosus is a temporary fetal blood vessel that hooks up the pulmonary artery to the aorta. When this does not close at birth or shortly thereafter, the baby has what is known as a PDA. The treatment varies from patient to patient: if the PDA is large, it is much harder on the baby's heart.

The usual course for infants is first using a medication known as **Indomethacin**. If this does not close the PDA and it's still too large and causing issues for the baby, a common surgical procedure will right this condition.

In recent years, the PDA has been a source of controversy, and the value of closing it has been debated a great deal by **neonatologists** (*see below*).

DEB'S TAKE:

The PDA was a constant concern throughout Becky's NICU stay and during the "rollercoaster" ride this issue made sure to rear its ugly head more than once. Thankfully, the **Indomethacin** helped and Becky avoided the PDA procedure.

NICOLE'S TAKE:

Nicholas's PDA, unfortunately, did not close for almost 2 years. We literally had three different hospitals telling us three different things that went something like this:

Hospital A: If you don't proceed with the PDA surgery you will be considered "negligent parents," as they believed that was the chief reason Nicholas was in failure to thrive.

Hospital B: If you proceed with the PDA surgery your son won't make it out of the surgery alive, and, if he does, the risk of having a huge seizure during the procedure could make Nicholas a vegetable.

Hospital C: Let's wait and see. He's too small and fragile for the surgery and we may just be lucky—even though his PDA should have grown over by now, it hasn't, but you never know, it might just do it.

Nicholas's PDA did finally close, and thank God he never had to go through yet another surgery. However, this illustration shows parents

that they are often going to be put in the very unenviable position of making hard decisions with even harsher responses from medical staff while trying to make those decisions. Follow your heart, and gut to see which of the medical professionals you most closely align with regarding any contradictory information you're hearing.

- What is the procedure to correct a PDA?
- How long does the procedure take and how is my child cared for during this procedure?
- What is the recovery time from this procedure and how will it affect my baby's discharge date?
- Will my child require medications or other therapies after the procedure?
- What can I do to help my child through this?
- Are there any long-term effects I should be aware of regarding this condition and/or this procedure?
- Who will be performing this procedure and what is his/her background and success rate?

NOTES:

Perforated Bowel/Perfing:
A common occurrence that cause the intestines to erupt or break down from **Necrotizing Enterocolitis (NEC)**.

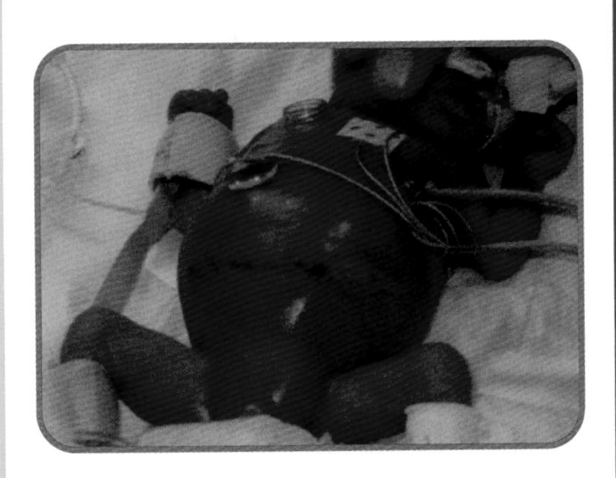

Nicholas's stoma—post-NEC surgery
Photo Credit: Brian Hoven

Peripheral IV:
An IV that is positioned away from the **central lines**, usually in the hand or foot, occasionally in the scalp.

Peripherally Inserted Central Catheter (PICC Line):
A line or catheter that is inserted at the vein in the baby's arm that runs through several larger veins, finally opening up into the right atrium of the heart. Used as another way to deliver **IV** feedings or medication if your baby needs a longer-term solution in terms of delivering IV fluids, nutrition, or medications.

Periventricular-Intraventricular Hemorrhage (PV-IVH):
*See **Brain Bleed***. Even if your baby has had clear head sonograms after birth, PV-IVH can still occur. For this reason, a subsequent sonogram is done around the 30 week mark. Check with your **neonatologist** for the head sonogram schedule so that you may rule out PV-IVH.

Petechiae:
Pronounced [pə-tē'kē-ə], these are tiny (<3 mm) round, red pinpoints that show bleeding under the skin and are often seen post-birth in infants who are either violently coughing or vomiting. The indications are many and can be something very minor or something more serious. Medications may also cause this finding.

All NICU patients develop red-spots somewhere on the skin, but they are rarely Petechiae. If you see any such spots on your baby, be sure to bring it to the doctor's attention.

NICOLE'S TAKE:

I got back from the hospital café, and when I looked at Nicholas it looked like someone had taken a fine ball point pen and dotted little spots all over his cheeks and forehead. I was later told it was from the pressure of his vomiting and he had formed **Petechiae**. They were amazingly uniform and he actually looked quite festive from them!

Phototherapy:
The "lights" under which your baby goes to relieve **jaundice**.

Physical Therapist:
A specialist who will work with your baby's **gross motor skills** development.

- How is my child developing at this time?
- Is there anything I can do to help my child at bedside?

- What types of therapies are you providing my child at this time and/or in the future?
- Is there anything else I should know at this time?

NOTES:

____
____
____
____
____
____
____
____
____
____

- Are there any long-term concerns I should be aware of with this illness?
- Is there anything else I should know at this time?

NOTES:

____
____
____
____
____
____
____
____
____
____

Pneumonia:
Your baby may develop this infection in the lungs. If so, the doctors will take ongoing x-rays while treating your baby with antibiotics. This is one of the major and ongoing chronic health concerns for Preemie babies—especially for those on the vent.

- What is being done at this point to help my child recover?
- What can I do to help my child during this illness?

Pneumothorax:
A collapsed lung that may have been the result of changes in pressure in the chest cavity.

Polycythemia:
Condition in which the blood has too many red blood cells (opposite of anemia).

Positional Plagiocephaly:
A condition where your child's head has been flattened on a particular side and is misshapen. Preemies are at risk for this condition so make sure your NICU staff members are keeping an eye on this. Your pediatrician should also be looking for signs of this con-

dition as well. You may hear staff referring to a child's head shape as "Toaster Head" or other such vernacular. Don't be offended by it…slang just comes with the territory.

CAPPS (Craniofacial Condition Specific Specialist Directory): www.cappskids.org

Capps Kids is a great resource for parents wanting to learn more about head deformities and where to get help.

DEB'S TAKE:

Becky did have some flattening to her skull, especially after the NICU. My husband and I believe this was due to her not only being a Preemie but also to her being on her back for sleep out of concern of preventing **Sudden Infant Death Syndrome (SIDS)**. A neurosurgeon took one look at her and stated she would be fine and would round out by three years old. Regardless of the flattening, Gregg and I never put her down to sleep on anything other than her back. A breathing baby was more important to us than a baby with a nicely shaped skull.

In the NICU, Nicole playfully called rolled up diapers and Squishons (gel pillows) "NICU furniture" and arranged these support items around Nicholas's sides, stomach, and shoulders. Nicole would continually move Nicholas's head for him from side to side, so that he never rested too long in one space. Get in the habit of moving your baby's head in such a manner and you will help maintain a good shape for his head. It's also much more comfortable for the baby to be moved from time to time, and you must remember that if he is on the **vent**, it is very hard for him to manage easy movement. Remember to ask your nurse first.

Preemie (aka Premature Baby/ Premature Infant):
Any baby born prior to 37 weeks' gestation is deemed premature. The level of prematurity is based on gestational age at birth and falls within measured guidelines for **weight**. (*For a full breakdown, see **What is a Preemie/Micro-Preemie?**, page 96.*)

Primary Care Physician and/or Primary Care Nurse (PCP):
The main "go-to" doctor and/or nurse for your baby. Because you will be dealing with doctors on rotation (periods of time from 2-4 weeks or more), you will

be constantly hearing a different doctor's assessment and care plan for your baby when you are in larger hospitals with multiple **neonatologists**.

Just as it is important to obtain a primary nurse/s for your baby, it is critical that you have a primary neonatologist to maintain the global care for your baby if your baby was born so early that it is clear she will be living in the NICU for the next several months. You will often have more than one primary nurse if you stay at the hospital very long. If your baby has a complicated medical course, you will usually have an AM and PM primary nurse. This is important for many reasons, chief being **continuity of care**. If you find you are disagreeing with one of the rotating neonatologists, you can go to the primary doctor who may then intervene. Having a primary neonatologist is new for some hospitals as is the concept of **family-centered care** (where the family is a very integral component of your baby's care program, currently available in very few hospitals).

NICOLE'S TAKE:

Day 45 and I discover my favorite nurse. Becky is young and energetic and utterly devoted to the development of the babies. "It's my thing," she repeats over and over as she tells me how to tweak Nicholas's cheek before he eats to prepare him for suckling. She explains that the reason Nicholas tends to desat on one side repeatedly is because he's gotten used to one side and his neck is stiff.

"Your two worst issues are going to be the vent and getting him off it and then dealing with his tracheal response. Those tubes get very sore. The second thing is going to be the feeds. And let me tell ya, it will be so hard to see him go up, then down, up then down."

This is his third day of trophic feeds—the most he has ever done. His one little cc has been upped to every three hours and he's grooving on it. He's taking all of his feeds without a bit of residuals. I'm ecstatic.

"Hey Mom, since your son is doing so well today and I have to change his isolette, do you want to hold him?"

Do I want to get down on my knees and kiss her orthopedic clogs? Do I want to take a meeting with Barbara Streisand?

Becky and I soon fall into a regular routine. I will ask her if it's a three-margarita day or a four-margarita day when it's been a particularly stressful time. She'll give me the an-

swer and I call her husband at home and give him her drink order. We become so familiar with one another that one day I mock-yell at her that she's not taking care of my son. I discover another mom on the bay thinks I'm a total b--ch. But that's how we survive. Humor and margaritas.

Pulmonary Edema:
Essentially fluid in the lungs. The build up of fluid in the lungs can also be a sign of heart failure and can be evidenced by swelling in the body.

Pulmonary Hemorrhage:
Occurs when there is bleeding in the lungs. This is an acute situation which requires immediate attention and action.

Pulmonologist:
A doctor who specializes and cares for the lungs and respiratory (breathing) system.

Pulse Oximeter (Pulse-Ox):
A sensor that measures the amount of oxygen in the blood. Usually threaded around the large toe or thumb (or, if your baby is a **Micro-Preemie**, around their entire foot).

Radiologist:
The specialist that takes and/or reads your baby's X-rays.

Referral:
When a doctor wants your baby to see a specialist in a given area they will write an order for a referral (suggest a specialist by name) who can treat your baby's specific medical issue(s).

Reflux (also known as GERD and Acid Reflux):
While not uncommon for normal birth babies, this is one of the standard plights of the Preemie as their digestive system is overly sensitive and has not developed appropriate maturity. Should it become constant or when a Preemie has not yet learned to protect their own airways, reflux and **GERD** can become a life altering and threatening condition.

Reflux 101 by Jan Gambino, M.Ed.
Amazon.com

Registry Nurse (RN):
You may hear a nurse referred to as a “registry” nurse (though this term is not used universally in this country, so they may go by other names in your hospital). These are nurses who are assigned by an agency that places temp workers. While many registry nurses are excellent, if your baby is in critical condition, you should never be assigned a registry nurse as they are unfamiliar with both your baby and the hospital itself. If such an assignment occurs, see the charge nurse and request one of your “regulars.” If that is not possible ask for a nurse that at least is a staffer.

NICOLE’S TAKE:

Two days ago a registry nurse who looked like she was on the unhappy side of a hangover sat at the nurse’s computer at the back of the bay looking up flights on the internet as two of the babies she had under her care were **desatting**. When one of them began to **brady** down (heart rate falling below 80) one of the older staffers assigned to Nicholas that day snapped at her, “Your baby is **bradying**.”

Twenty seconds later she repeated: “Your baby is bradying!”

The registry nurse didn’t even blink. Not even after the third time.

I made the staffer promise me she would not leave the room again. I later find out that they are not allowed to leave a registry nurse alone in the ward. But I’ve seen it happen. Time and again. These nurses need their breaks after all. All the more reason you should try to be at the hospital as often as possible.

Resident:
A doctor who has completed medical school and is continuing his training in his medical specialty. There are excellent residents, but they are also still learning. Since the resident is more than likely doing their rotation in this area without intending to specialize in this specific branch of **neonatology**, you may find your NICU nurse (and his/her wealth of experience) to be a stronger resource.

It’s okay to question a **resident**. We had many residents who told us they wanted to run from the NICU ward and that, if it weren’t for them having to go through this specific rotation, they would never in a million years choose this specialty. Politely ask questions, and if you get the sense they are in over their head, ask to speak to your **primary nurse and/or doctor**. Don't be afraid to ask the same question of a dozen people until you get an answer that "clicks" with you. By the time Nicholas and I were in our fourth month in the NICU, we were teaching the residents!

Residuals:
The amount of feeding left in the stomach after some period of time, usually two hours. It is what your baby is unable to eat: These leftovers allow the doctors to know how well your baby is digesting and feeding.

Respiration:
The act of breathing or one breath cycle (inhalation and exhalation).

Respiratory Distress Syndrome (RDS):
A potentially life-threatening condition in which the lungs are unable to provide enough oxygen for the baby's blood. This is quite common in premature babies since their lungs are underdeveloped when they are born. The infant will be put on **ventilators** or a **CPAP** to help lessen the severity of this condition.

Respiratory Syncytial Virus (RSV):
An illness initially resembling a modest cold in adults. It can be dangerous for newborns—and even worse for Preemies—since it is highly contagious and complications from the virus can develop into a major respiratory infection. At the time of this publication premature infants born at 29 weeks or below are eligible to receive special injections to help prevent RSV.

- What is being done for my child at this time?
- Is there anything I need to be concerned at this point?
- What can I do to help my child?
- Are there long-term consequences with this illness that I should be aware of?
- Is there anything else I should know at this time?

NOTES:

The Centers for Disease Control's RSV Information:
http://www.cdc.gov/RSV/

The March of Dimes:
http://www.marchofdimes.com/pnhec/298_9546.asp

Respiratory Therapist (RT):
A specialist in the area of breathing who will often give your baby breathing treatments and help with the care and placement of the **ventilator**. Often they will also suction your baby to get rid of the fluids that build up in the lungs.

Respite Care:
Parents of special needs babies need a break but often cannot because their baby requires special trained care. Respite care provides that break and is usually provided by any number of state, local, and county programs.

Find your local respite at https://archrespite.org/

Resuscitation:
See ***Cardiopulmonary Resuscitation (CPR)***.

Retinopathy of Prematurity (ROP):
An eye disease that affects the Preemie population. ROP has a number of stages and can ultimately lead to vision damage or even partial/full blindness as a result of ***too*** much oxygen, or frequently changing blood levels of oxygen and carbon dioxide.

- When your baby is on a **ventilator** or **CPAP**, his or her medical team will be keeping the oxygen levels where they need to be.
- If your baby does develop ROP, there is now laser surgery that can help. Moreover, as of this writing, trials are underway evaluating a chemical injection into the eye to reverse this disease process.
- If your baby is at risk for this disease, he or she will undergo an eye exam in the NICU and will most likely require more exams as follow-up at the eye specialist's office.
- Even if your baby is only at-risk for ROP upon discharge, it is extremely important that you make any and all required follow-up visits with the optometrist.

preemieworld

- Pediatric Retinal Research Foundation: ***www.pediatricrrf.org/***
- National Federation for the Blind: ***www.nfb.org***
- Wayfinder Family Services: ***https://www.wayfinderfamily.org/***

If A Diagnosis Has Yet To Be Made:

- Is my baby at risk for ROP?
- If they are at risk, when will the specialist do the eye exam?
- When will you know that he is no longer at risk for ROP?
- Is there anything I can do to make my baby more comfortable during this exam?

NOTES:

If Your Baby Has Been Diagnosed With ROP:

- What stage is the ROP?
- What interventions are to be taken to help my baby with ROP?
- What is my baby's prognosis with ROP?
- How I can help my baby in the NICU and at home?

NOTES:

DEB'S TAKE:

Becky was at risk for **ROP** and so an eye exam was done in the NICU and at several follow-up visits post-NICU.

My advice is do not walk but *run* to your child's eye doctor for these follow-up visits. Timing is everything and could help your child save his sight in a complicated situation. If you can make the appointment prior to discharge that would be fabulous. Ask your doctor for the number of days after discharge that your child is to be seen by the eye doctor.

If the eye doctor does not have appointments available stress the urgency due to your child having been a Preemie. If you still get a less than acceptable response, ask to talk to the office manager. Beyond that your child's **neonatologist** or pediatrician may be able to assist with this as well.

NICOLE'S TAKE:

Nicholas was severely affected by his ROP and he almost completely lost his eyesight. While the surgeon was able to save Nicholas' retina from detaching his ROP had so progressed that he became severally myopic. With the help of glasses with 22/27 lenses!—Nicholas makes his way through the world with amazing accuracy. Children are so resilient and adapt. One day Gabrielle wondered how Nicholas "sees everything" so we all decided to wear glasses to check out his world!

We share the world through Nicholas's eyes
Photo Credit: Danielle Marbury

Retracted Breathing /Retracting:
When you can see the rib cage pumping up and down and the infant is working way too hard to breathe. They are not breathing in a normal rhythm, but rather from their stomachs. You can see them retract through nostrils flaring and the rib cage pumping up and down. When it's severe you may actually be able to count the ribs. The infant is in **respiratory distress**. Breathing treatments can often decrease or resolve the retractions.

Rooming-In:
Prior to Discharge Day; this is a red letter night. Your hospital may provide you with the opportunity to take care of your baby without the help of medical staff. This is especially important if you have been living at the hospital for months on

preemieworld

end. Your NICU may have a separate room that can be used for you to stay overnight with your baby in order to care for him or her. This gives you a chance to take care of your baby overnight with staff right nearby in case you need help.

Rounds/Rounding with Doctors:
When the doctor discusses patients with the fellows, residents, interns, nurses, and particular specialists (cardiologist, nutritionist, etc.). ask if you may listen to the rounds discussion about your baby; if your doctor does not permit this, ask why they do not allow it.

NICOLE'S TAKE:

Rounding with the doctors may not be as easy as I suggest. When I began to round with the doctors, I was the only mother doing so. There are natural barriers to entry here: How well one can grasp medical information and jargon, how emotionally spent you are, and how inclined you are to put one more thing on your plate. Let's not forget it also depends on how willing a doctor is to include your participation in rounding.

The best way to decrease the feelings of helplessness is to shed some of the components over which we have no control. Gaining a sense of empowerment in this kind of situation will help you immensely. Gathering this new information and utilizing a combination of lay person's medicine and intuition will help you gain the confidence you need to see if you agree with the doctor and, if not, to make suggestions.

Scleral Buckle:
A procedure performed to prevent retinal detachment.

Seizure:
When the brain cannot control certain electrical activity. There are many different types of seizures, including those caused by a disrupted nervous system, fevers, birth defects, and oxygen deficits. These can be as extreme as huge physical convulsions or as mild as minor physical disturbances. While over 50% of seizures are unidentifiable, there are many medications that they can give your baby to help resolve and decrease the seizure activity.

Sepsis (Septic):
Blood infection, indicating that the baby is sick and can worsen very quickly. Usually at the first sign of sepsis, the doctors will begin antibiotics.

NICOLE'S TAKE:

We didn't even realize Nicholas had what we now refer to as an "undiagnosed **seizure** disorder," until well after we were home. And then we discovered he simply could not function when we tried to remove his Phenobarbital and Clonapin. But with both of these medications, whatever seizure disorder he is experiencing is kept under control.

We speak with so many other Preemie parents who say the same thing; our children are disabled, but in a way specific and unique to Preemie children. They often do not follow the same diagnoses or patterns of other disabilities and oftentimes health care professionals have difficulty in understanding how to treat Preemie Kids since they don't fall into known categories and everything about the way Preemies grow and develop is so new.

Sepsis (Septic):
Blood infection, indicating that the baby is sick and can worsen very quickly. Usually at the first sign of sepsis, the doctors will begin antibiotics.

Short Bowel Syndrome (SBS):
Condition resulting from the partial loss of the intestine, in turn causing malabsorption of food received by your baby. If the malabsorption is severe enough, doctors will more than likely need another way to deliver food, usually through an IV method. The loss of intestine is usually the result of **Necrotizing Enterocolitis (NEC)**, in which the surgeon must remove a portion of the intestine.

The normal length of the small intestine is 200 to 250 cm for an infant of 35 weeks; 100 to 120 cm for a premature infant at less than 30 weeks' gestation. If your baby loses more than 80% of the small intestine, they will more than likely require **IV parenteral nutrition** support and may not survive.

Shunt:
A medical device in the form of a hole or tube that allows drainage from one part of the body to another.

Small for Gestational Age (SGA):
Pretty self-explanatory, this may be a factor of intrauterine malnutrition (not enough calories or oxygen getting to the fetus), as well as a common result of twin or higher order (triplets and above) multiple births.

Social Security Income (SSI):
This is part of the social security system and can pay out some extra mon-

ey to help with expenses of a disabled child. There are requirements for this and more information can be found at: ***https://www.ssa.gov/***.

As of this writing, babies at a birth weight of 2 lbs, 10 oz might be eligible. Talk to your Social Worker for more information.

Spinal Tap:
A delicate medical procedure wherein the doctor extracts spinal fluid from within the spinal canal to test for infections such as **meningitis**. The infant is usually sedated because they cannot move during the procedure.

Sprinting:
Slang often used to describe the time a baby is off oxygen or a **ventilator** and allowed to breath spontaneously or be put on room air, perhaps for fifteen minutes each hour, or one hour every three hours depending on how well the baby is able to oxygenate his or her own systems.

Stabilization:
Nurses are rotated into this position and stabilize babies coming in from delivery, nursery, or transport. They also take over for other nurses on breaks, etc.

Step Down Unit:
Also known as the "Feeders and Growers Unit," this is one of the many steps toward preparing for Discharge Day. At this time your nurses might start to teach you how to bathe your baby and do other more "normal" parenting activities. Discharge may still be days or weeks away, but this is a big milestone.

Stoma (Abbrev. for Ileostomy):
From **ileostomy**, the hole for feces. It is folded over unprotected skin, so it's important to keep it as clean as possible and to change frequently so as to keep your baby's intestinal fluids from breaking down their fragile skin.

Suck-Swallow Pattern:
Describes the efficient manner of eating that **OT**s will teach your baby once they are off the **venti-lator**. The muscles are often weak around their mouths after long vent stints, thereby making it difficult for them to create a strong vacuum for sucking from a bottle or nipple. They also have difficulties under-standing how to swallow and pro-tect their airways (which could lead to **aspirating** formula), so it is very important to have the OT and/or feeding specialist work with your baby before you go home.

Suction:
The act of removing phlegm and mu-cus from the infant's lungs so that they might breathe better. Suction-ing is usually done by a **respiratory**

therapist and/or nurse. It's done more often if a baby is coming down with an infection and producing more mucus and phlegm.

Sudden Infant Death Syndrome (SIDS):
A real syndrome for which Preemies are at high risk. You will notice that the nurses might put your baby on their stomach during part of each day—because the baby is hooked up to monitors, they can act quickly if there is a cessation of breathing that leads to SIDS. At home you do not have that luxury.

As of this writing, it is known that putting a baby on their back to sleep is the proper sleeping position. No blankets, stuffed animals or any other type of article of bedding should be in the crib. There is a wide range of sleep sacks specifically designed for warmth without posing a risk. Get these before Discharge Day (or hint to family and friends that this would make a great baby shower gift).

- **First Candle:** ***www.FirstCandle.org***
- **American SIDS Institute:** ***www.SIDS.org***

Of course you are thinking right about now, "This is great information but what about the grandparents? They won't listen to me." This is a great topic to discuss with your team and see if they would bring it up with the grandparents when they visit the unit.

Surfactant:
This is a complex substance given to your baby through the **ET Tube** after birth. This substance provides your baby with the extra boost toward stability of the lungs. Surfactant is normally made by the lungs, but it is insufficient in premature babies. In the absence of enough surfactant, the lungs tend to collapse, making breathing difficult. Doctors therefore give one or more doses of surfactant to help the lungs until the baby starts making more surfactant.

Suspicious:
Slang response to test results that make a doctor feel like something might be wrong. (*See* ***Not Impressed***)

Symmetric Growth Restriction:
Condition where growth of the baby has uniformly been restricted throughout the entire body and organs. If you hear this term applied to your baby, ask your doctor what that means for him or her.

Tegaderm:
Life saving clear tape used for affixing

medical paraphernalia to your baby including cannula, **stoma** bags, and **IV**s. Amazing stuff!

Therapy:
Anything done to treat your baby for any condition. Most commonly, therapy is used to help stimulate your baby's body to heal itself and catch-up in developmental milestones. You may find that your baby's NICU has therapists on staff to help with this and/or that your baby will be prescribed a variety of therapies to receive once home. All of it is helpful and will make a difference for your baby down the road.

Types of Therapy

- Occupational Therapy
- Physical Therapy
- Speech Therapy
- Vision Therapy
- Music Therapy
- Feeding Specialists

- Will my baby need therapy in the NICU?

- Will my baby need therapy after going home?
- If yes, what types of therapy are needed and why?
- In addition to therapy, what types of things can I do on my own to help my baby?

NOTES:

____

____

____

Total Parenteral Nutrition (TPN):
TPN gives your baby their total maximum calories broken down into proteins, dextrose and lipids, electrolytes, and minerals. This food is a literally a lifesaver and delivered by **IV** instead of through a feeding tube or bottle.

DEB'S TAKE:

Upon seeing my daughter for the first time I was taken aback by her alien-likeness with the **CPAP** stuck in her nose. And then there was the **IV** and the "padding" around it to keep her

preemieworld

from pulling it out. She looked like she had a homemade fly swatter/ bee keeper glove on her arm as she swung it about. That's my girl, not even born yet and already swatting at things. I wonder if there is such a thing as a NICU Preemie light saber for parents that are Star Wars fans?

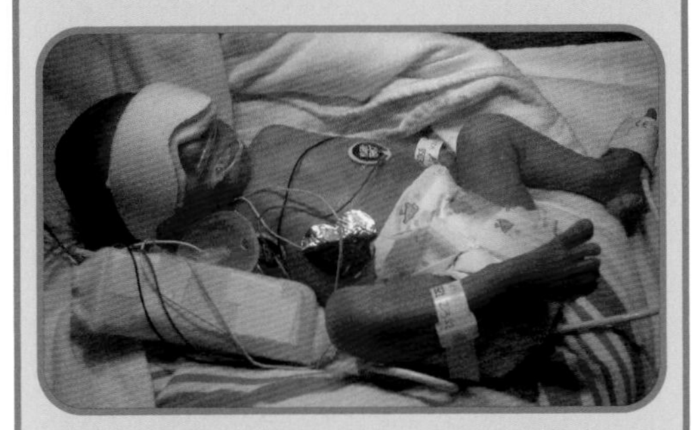

Becky with the IV "padding"
Photo Credit: Gregg Discenza

Touch Time:
A NICU term that describes that oh-too-brief period of time where parents get to finally see and touch their baby, after hours of being in **minimum stimulation**. This usually happens to babies who are born prior to 32 weeks. While seeing their infant for only those few moments is agony for all moms and parents, it is absolutely necessary for baby's well-being. One must be very careful when touching the skin of these small babies: the skin is so new and fresh it can be painful for them to feel your touch if you are not extremely gentle. Imagine how fragile their skin is if you can see right through it.

A common explanation some nurses use to dissuade you from needing to touch your son or daughter is that "your **bonding** was interrupted."

It may have been interrupted but it isn't broken, and you should pursue repairing and making it as strong as possible. You have every right to touch your baby.

If you are told that your touch is "dangerous" or "harming" the infant in any way, ask them to show you how to touch properly. If a nurse tells you not to touch your baby, ask to speak with a doctor. There are few circumstances, even when a baby is critically ill, when touch is not reassuring to the family and helpful for the baby. Even when your baby needs rest, gentle stroking may enhance that rest.

TPA:
A medicine used to break down a clot in the **Broviac**, usually at the point of entry. This is a sort of hysterical dilemma for moms: their baby has a **central IV** line that dumps right into the heart stream. One must have that **central line** in order to receive nutrition or oftentimes life saving medica-

tions. But because the central lines and Broviacs are made out of plastics and foreign materials to the infant's body, they are very likely to cause clots, which can, in turn, not only block the central line from use but serve as a breeding place for highly opportunistic infections like **MRSA (Methicillin Resistant Staphylococcus Aureus)**.

The problem is that the doctor must find a way to configure ***precisely*** how much TPA he or she needs to administer: just enough to push into the line to reach the clot, but not so much that it spills over into the heart and blood stream.

Transfusion:
The replenishment of your baby's blood supply by infusing additional blood.

Blood is a rare commodity. Every hospital will have their own blood bank, but they are usually short on blood. The entire time we were at the NICU we would see notices about shortages. Preemie blood requires additional requirements and more rigorous standards. The best thing your friends and family can do for your baby is to give blood as often as they can. When you're ready, consider giving blood as well.

NICOLE'S TAKE:

We were blessed to have three main blood donors for Nicholas. The three women who gave so selflessly of their blood and time not only matched Nicholas's blood type but were also **CMV** negative. The interesting thing about two of the three donors is that neither my partner nor I had been in contact with them that much at the time.

Yet they gave and gave again. Nicholas required so much blood in his early days and thereafter (even after we had left the NICU). When he had to return for all his surgeries, these same saints gave again and again. Nicholas's godmother, Victoria Alonso, was the one donor we saw fairly often. She would go out

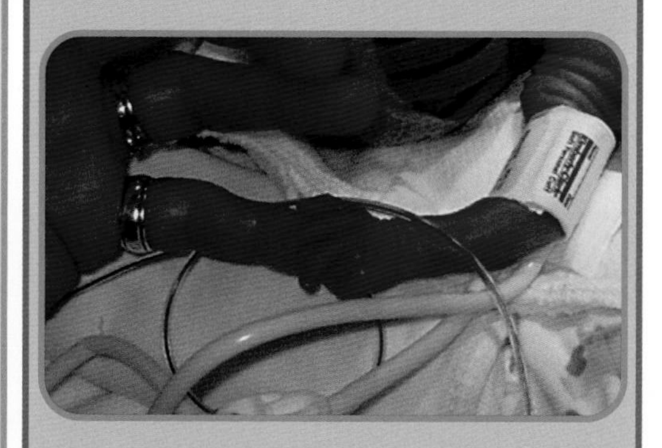

Nicholas gets another much needed transfusion
Photo Credit: Brian Hoven

and eat huge thick steaks to get her blood "pumped full of iron." Give blood as often as you can. Remember your baby may need someone's blood, and you can return the favor in this way.

Nicholas's first blood transfusion was only 3 cc's—less than a full teaspoon. When I heard this I truly appreciated the scale of this medicine and how small a **Micro-Preemie** really is!

DEB'S TAKE:

When Becky required a blood **transfusion** my husband and I were obviously nervous but signed off on the paperwork anyway. As teenagers we had learned all about issues with blood. I wish that I had donated blood prior to getting pregnant so that I knew what I know now: blood banks are extremely careful about who can and who cannot donate.

There are all sorts of screens in place to protect the patients from receiving tainted blood. Today I donate regularly and just started donating platelets. I do this in honor of Becky and the selfless person that gave up his hour of life to donate blood so my daughter could live.

UA Line/ UAC (Umbilical Arterial Line/Umbilical Artery Catheter): Initially at birth, the first arterial line is placed in an umbilical artery. This is a much better way to determine **blood pressures** and measure **blood gases** and other lab values. Blood samples can be drawn with very little pain in this manner.

Donna was the mother of a 29-weeker IUGR baby who had a **UA line** in her son's belly button. One of drawbacks to this type of line is the possibility of blood not getting to extremities. Jonah's feet in fact turned very blue. This was complicated by the fact that he was African American and throughout the night no one noticed that blood flow had decreased to the point that his toes had lost all circulation. Jonah lost his three middle toes. Donna, a battle-scarred veteran of the NICU smiled wearily as she removed the blanket to reveal Jonah's toeless foot and murmured, "Well, look at the bright side—he can still play the violin…"

preemieworld

a b c d e f g h i j k l m n o p q r s t u **v** w x y z

Ventilator (Vent):
The machine that breathes for your baby, the ventilator is the reason that so many premature babies can now actually survive. Preemies born before 28 weeks will more than likely be put on a ventilator. Depending on medical challenges that your baby has, they may be put on the ventilator at any gestational age if needed to help the baby breathe.

There are a wide variety of specialized ventilators with a veritable menagerie of settings to support the most critically damaged and underdeveloped lungs. Popular vent terms include: High Frequency, Jet, Oscillator Vents, Intermittent Mandatory Ventilation (IMV), and **Liquid Ventilation**.

Many Preemies will require help with breathing. Depending on how premature your baby is any number of breathing devices may be used even if only for a few hours. A great percentage of Preemies are born with undeveloped lungs. While we don't give a second thought to breathing, it's hard work for a Preemie to move the diaphragm muscles. And the brain center that controls breathing as an autonomic process isn't fully switched on yet.

But how does the air get into the baby's lungs? A doctor must insert a breathing or **ventilator** tube. This tube goes right down into the baby's lungs so that breathing can be done for them. When your baby is taken from the delivery room to the neonatal unit, they will attach this tube to a ventilator. This machine will now take over for the human who was pumping oxygen into your little one's lungs.

Ventriculoperitoneal Shunt (VP Shunt):
A tube placed in the brain used to relieve pressure on the brain by draining the extra fluid to the abdomen. (*See* ***Hydrocephalus***.)

Visiting Nurses:
Your NICU may prescribe for your baby to receive visits from a visiting nurse during the first few weeks at home. Consider it a nurse that makes house calls, can check the baby, and answer your questions.

How to Make Your Nurse Visits More Efficient:

- Keep a list of questions.
- Have a copy of your Discharge Med-

- ical Summary prepared for them.
- Have your insurance card ready for them to collect the information.
- Try to schedule visits so that you are not interrupting sleep time for you and most importantly for your baby. Be clear with the **Visiting Nurse** about this and see if they can schedule around "wake time" if that is regularly occurring.

Wean:
To wean from the ventilator means pushing the settings closer and closer to simulate room air to get the baby stronger before they **extubate** or pull out the **ET tube**.

Weight:
Welcome to one of the many new obsessions during your baby's NICU stay! From the second you know your baby's birth weight you will be watching it go up and down. And down and up. This depends on a variety of factors. Eating, urinating, defecating, vomiting—it all counts and can change the weight rapidly. *(See **gram** for a conversion chart of grams into pounds and ounces.)*

Wet Weight:
This is the weight you see on the scale without taking into account the factors listed above.

Dry Weight:

This is your baby's actual weight within the margin of error for a practiced **neonatologist**. They will study your baby's chart, looking at the "ins" (which consist of food, fluids, medicines, **transfusions**) and the "outs" (urine, vomiting, etc.) and make a determination if your baby appears to be holding water or swelling. They may deduct 100 to 200 grams from the weight that showed up on the scale, considered inflated weight, to make medication dosing as precise as possible.

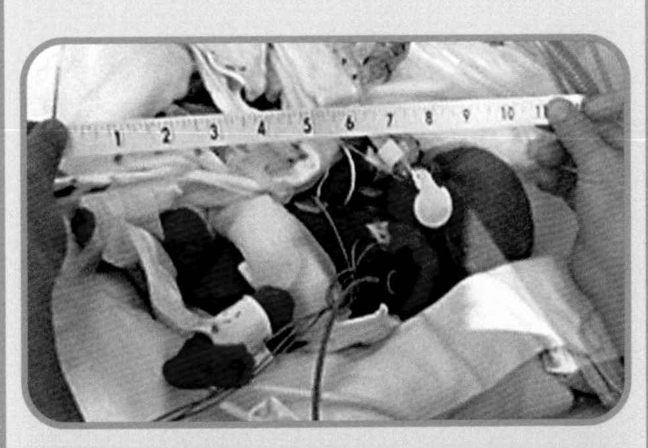

Wet weight (top)
and dry weight (bottom)
Photo Credit: Brian Hoven

preemieworld

IV.

THE NICU:

YOUR BABY'S WOMB IN A ROOM

The NICU

"No matter how many pictures we send up to L&D [Labor and Delivery], you can't envision how small they actually are until you've seen it with your own two eyes."

—KJ Cedars Charge Nurse

You've heard the term. Perhaps it was a catchphrase on the 6:00 news or in a feature magazine article. You vaguely understand that this is a baby born early. But the pictures you've seen are horrifying. You turn the pages and flip the channels as quickly as possible to erase the image from your head.

But now you have just had a Preemie. Now what?

When you first see your infant, he or she will probably look much different than you expect. You have been waiting for the same cuddly ball of "oohs" and "aaahs" you had envisioned as you watched "The Baby Story"—or had with your first child.

It is difficult to prepare for that first moment. Depending on how premature your baby is, this first contact will impact you in various ways. If your infant is only a few weeks early, he will simply be a smaller version of the bundle of joy you expect, perhaps much skinnier than you expected. But if your little one is born at 30, 28, 25, even 23 weeks, it will be a shocking sight.

It's not just that your baby looks nothing like a baby, that he appears to be the wisp of a froglike bird: He is, in fact, still a fetus.

When you first see this wriggling, waif-like being, you may not be able to truly digest the scale. He's so small all you see is a dangly foot. Her crimped hand is the size of a Cheerio. And as quickly as the baby is displayed to you, a neonatal team and labor and delivery staff whisk her away to a small table to prep for the NICU. In your post-labor delirium, it looks like children greedily descending upon piñata candy.

That this sweet little thing—the latest new member of your family—looks nothing like you or your spouse may be the image you are left with. And you can't help but think:

Was it all a bad dream?

preemieworld

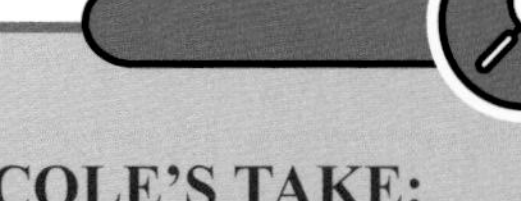

NICOLE'S TAKE:

"Oh, my God," I think. *"He's…he's magnificent. A perfect miniature being."*

"He's losing color!" someone shouts at the resuscitation table.

"Come on people!" Another barks.

My heart yanks sideways. I understand now. The hard part is just beginning.

"Nicholas, please…please stay with me."

Ka-swish. Ka-swish. Ka-swish.

As we pass the ten minute mark, they continue bagging.

"We will only resuscitate up to 15 minutes—as a matter of ethics."

A gloved hand performs my son's breathing, the measured pumping a practiced metronome.

"We need a 2.5 for intubation!"

"We don't stock 'em that small."

I can't see Nicholas in the flurry—the constant motion of scrubs as hands fly in and around his small table: a huddle of doctors furiously working to save my son.

This wasn't supposed to be happening for months. How can a baby even be born or survive this early?

"I'm here for you little man... Whatever you need...I'm here...I love you..."

"I've got one!"

Everyone stands aside as a respiratory therapist barges in with a tube the size of a Swizzle Stick for Nicholas's intubation. I glance at the digital clock. It's pushing twelve minutes. There's more bagging, more medical jargon I don't understand, and then the words are all too clear:

"He's still not breathing!"

"He's losing color."

I feel time choking in on us.

These thirteen and a half minutes become the longest time span of my life. I'm jolted back to reality by a gruff voice: "Mom, come meet your new son."

Nicholas turns to look at me.

Nicholas shortly after birth
Picture Credit: Brian Hoven

He opens his black sapphire eyes and grabs my pinky in his rice-sized fingers.

"Nicole, he's looking right at you!" Dr. Chow proclaims in awe.

I feel the tug at my solar plexus.

It may not be medically possible but Nicholas sees me. His eyes laser into my own. Certainly he cannot be holding this kind of non-verbal dialogue. Undoubtedly it is something I'm imagining.

But his eyes do not waver as they lock into my own.

It doesn't help that, instead of baby buntings and stuffed animals, your new baby is flanked by stuff that's straight from the set of Star Trek (The Next Generation, of course). Hi-tech, science fiction **isolette** paraphernalia—the **monitors**, wires, leads—stuck to this little person's body makes it all appear even more unreal.

He may be on a **ventilator**. With her dangly little knees and arms flopped out wide, she looks so very similar to the splayed-out frogs you dissected in science class. They'll fight with the tube stuck down their gullet, wrestling frantically at times to rid themselves of the very thing that is saving their life.

You may feel repulsed. Ashamed. Terrified. Guilty.

No amount of talking, reading or explaining will ever truly prepare you for your first contact with this magical new being. Yet having an acceptance that you will travel the entire gamut of feelings in the coming days will help you accept where you are at today. Once you can stop asking, *"Why me? Why my poor baby?"* and deal in the here and now, the here and now will be a kinder, gentler place.

It will be hard to see your friends and family when they visit the hospital—no matter how many pictures you send, they won't be able to believe their eyes. They'll gasp and feel faint. They may even say that your baby looks like a Stan Winston special effect. As your mother's eyes adjust, you'll soon find how beautiful your child is, but you may still freak out at the site of another Preemie. When other mothers share war stories, it will shake you to the core. Taking some NICU lessons to heart, though, will help you face the other infants in the same boat as your own. And you'll remember that every single feeling you are having is absolutely okay, normal, and expected.

WHAT IS A PREEMIE/ MICRO-PREEMIE?

"Your baby knows your voice already, so don't be afraid to use it. Your infant needs to hear you and know that you are near."

—Primary Nurse for Nicholas

The medical community requires categorization of everything so that they may create statistics from which they can glean information. However, the science of neonatology is quite new and still in its infancy of study (no pun intended).

For a parent, the difference between having a 34-week Preemie and a 23-week Preemie is quite drastic. Certainly a **Micro-Preemie** will come with many more health challenges, but make no mistake, there is not much difference in terms of being thrust into the **Neonatal Intensive Care Unit (NICU)** unprepared, shaken and oftentimes lost whether you're at week 26 or 32. And while individual babies will have extremely different medical courses, the experience for a parent is universally brutal.

The NICU isn't limited to premature infants. Babies born with genetic syndromes, health issues, and drug-addict mothers are also part of this population. When you've been inducted into this rare group, there is no turning back—you can never be "un-NICU'ed." And once you step foot in these halls, you will be forever changed.

That is what this book is for. We're here to help you find a way to journey through this life-altering experience with your baby and make it to the other side—Discharge Day.

Preemies Fall Into Several Subcategories:

Normal Birth Weight	2,500-3,999 grams	> 5 pounds, 8 ounces
Low Birth Weight (LBW)	<2,500 grams	< 5 pounds, 8 ounces
Very Low Birth Weight (VLBW)	<1,500 grams	< 3 pounds, 5 ounces
Extremely Low Birth Weight (ELBW)	<1,000 grams	< 2 pounds, 3 ounces
Micro Preemie	< 800 grams	< 1 pound, 7 ounces

According to National Institutes of Health (NIH) and the World Health Organization

A QUICK REALITY CHECK

Before jumping in, realize that being in the NICU is akin to being in a war. Once you are stuck in a fox-hole together, neither race nor age nor socio-economic status matters compared to getting out of that fox-hole alive.

The NICU is a great equalizer. A parent is a parent is a parent. And parents who have kids who face medical challenges do not see anything other than their infant getting well. Certainly there are parents who behave badly, but the true mettle of people comes out in these life and death situations and most people are good at their core. Parents just want their kids to get well and to leave the hospital. You end up spending a lot of time in the hospital with these people and the staff members attending to you and their needs, and you can't find a kinder, warmer second family than the parents and staff in the NICU.

Also note that here the people cut right through the small talk and banter. There's no time for light exchanges of pleasantries—you're eager to talk about what matters and get to the heart of things, often sharing parts of yourself and family dynamic with perfect strangers. But you're not strangers because we're all in this together.

DEB'S TAKE:

I always think about the **NICU** sort of like being a special member of a club. When you meet another NICU parent, it's like meeting a fellow veteran with whom you've gone through the bloody battle together. There's a wonderful shorthand to your language and they get it.

I always respond to any parent who emails me and asks for help. It's not that I feel like it's an obligation—it's what you give back because there was a mom, dad, or nurse who helped you that one day where you thought if you had to hear another bad piece of news you really were going to lose it. It may not seem like a big deal, but that person performed a random act of kindness in that moment when you needed another human being to treat you with tenderness because you were alone and lost.

YOUR BABY'S NEW WOMB IN A ROOM

The human eye is not meant to see a fetus. We can observe the fetus when it is in the clinical presentation—a technical exercise if you will—and we can read up on them in medical texts, journal articles, and on the Internet. But to bear a fetus is not a thing that comes naturally. Fetuses are obviously supposed to remain in the mother until they are fully "baked." However, when babies decide to make their entrance to the world, we must be prepared for them, no matter how early they might be.

NICOLE'S TAKE:

All I can really remember of the first 24 to 48 hours of his early little life, is gripping Nicholas's **isolette**. The glow of lights bathed his eight-inch long miniature frame, decked out in what looked like Model-T goggles and so much machinery he looked like a mini-borg in his little plastic bin.

Even though all this STUFF seems like an overwhelming barrier to entry to get to your child, it is absolutely necessary for his or her well-being.

Depending on how early you have had your baby, they will be living in one of the following:

INCUBATOR/ISOLETTE

The playwright Wendy Wasserstein most aptly named the **isolette** a "salad bin" in her now-famous essay: "Days of Awe: the Birth of Lucy Jane," about her own experience with the premature birth of her daughter.

The closest thing to a womb that medicine has come up with, **incubators** and isolettes, are amazing medical contraptions. They literally look as if the babies each have their own eco-system, complete with temperature control where your baby rests at a comfortable 98.6 degrees. You can see the condensation forming at the windows from the humidity kept to the perfect spot where your infant's very fragile skin will not be dried out or damaged. The wonderful thing about these womb simulators is that when the temperature or humidity drops, a monitor goes off to alert the nurses to adjust the "weather" conditions to accommodate your baby. It's also good to know whether your child is able to hold their own body temperature—a critical factor in being able to leave the isolette.

At first, you may find it almost impossible to work in the submarine window-hole confines of the isolette. You may also wonder how nurses can see anything in lighting made dim enough to simulate the womb. But as time goes by, you adjust and even

learn to change a diaper standing on one side in the dark.

INCUBATOR/ISOLETTE WITH MINIMUM STIMULATION PRECAUTIONS

This basically means your baby is covered for hours at a time protected from natural light in order to assimilate a darkened womb. (*See **Minimum Stimulation** below*)

OPEN ISOLETTE

These can be closed at night to maintain body temperature.

OPEN CRIB

In which your baby can have a crib much like he or she would have at home.

If your infant has been in the **isolette/incubator** for months prior to going to a crib, they will be carefully "weaned" into it.

It is absolutely critical that your baby not waste valuable calories—often difficult to gain in the first place and sometimes even more so to keep it on. These babies lose weight in a New York second! If they go to a crib too early and use all of their energy keeping themselves warm, they will drop any weight you've managed to put on them. When you are able to finally graduate your infant to a crib, it's a day for celebration, but try to make sure your infant can handle the transition before getting ahead of yourself.

Another factor to consider when weaning to a crib is the difference in temperatures inside the hospital (day and night). Nicholas could not be weaned for several weeks, because the nighttime temperatures at Cedars were several degrees below daytime temperatures. Make sure you're aware of these weather conditions.

Make your baby's crib as personal as you can. At the hospital, it's important for you to have as much of yourself, your family, and your home life as possible.

Since it is Nicole's family tradition that every baby start life out right with a Curious George monkey, the nurses allowed her to put the smallest version of the famed monkey—carefully sealed in a sanitized baggy—in Nicholas's **isolette** the day after he was born. She also placed photos of his mother, sister, etc., in a separate bag

so that he could be surrounded by family. His sister Gabrielle created several cards and drawings for him throughout his stay. By the time Nicholas was in his crib, he not only had a ton of wall hangings, he also had several toys and miniature speakers so that Nicole could play him recordings of Beethoven and Bach. Try to make the NICU your home away from home as much as possible and it will be that much more bearable.

THE MYRIAD OF MONITORS—AND HOW TO READ THEM

There are any number and type of monitors that will at first stun and overwhelm you. You will get confused because you'll think the **monitor** is beeping on your baby, and realize it's the baby next to you. You'll learn that monitors don't just beep, they have different levels of beeping (many of them designed to grow stronger and more alarming to convey the level of danger in which your infant might be).

The problem when you first get to the NICU is that you are so overwhelmed you don't even know what the beeping means. But as you begin to pick up information, you'll soon realize that one monitor is tracking your baby's heart rate, the other is making sure your baby is oxygenating sufficiently, that their "saturations" are holding steady.

Another might be a T-com monitor which tells you whether your baby is expiring too much carbon dioxide—one of the first signs that your infant is becoming ill. Yet another will let the medical staff know if your infant is having an **apnea**—meaning that she has stopped breathing on her own.

"Don't look at the monitor—look at the baby."

—Said at least once a day by the medical staff

It may seem like the most obvious of statements, but the reality is while we all (medical staff and parent) rely on the **monitors** to keep our infants safe and out of danger, they often malfunction. Old-timers will tell you they never did anything by the monitors back in the "old days." One look at the patient and they could more than likely tell what the problem was. While a nurse can tell that a patient isn't getting enough oxygen because they're turning blue, they cannot tell if a baby's

electrolytes are off, or how much carbon dioxide might be in the blood. Simply "looking at the patient" in today's medically-advanced world often cannot provide quite nuanced information that can be very important in treatment.

NICOLE'S TAKE:

Eventually the monitor sounds become less unnerving. At first I don't understand why the nurses don't leap tall buildings to observe the patient at every little beep. Then as time goes by I begin to hear the different sounds to the alarms and know which are important.

The only problem with the **monitors** is, once you become used to them, they can be a terrifying reminder of what's going on with your infant. You may be waiting to see your baby or to give him his next **breastfeeding** when the monitor suddenly alarms. You begin to sit in what we call Monitor-Combat-Readiness: the second you hear a single blare your neck tightens, your shoulders tense, and you want to immediately jump up and take care of your child. The beeping continues and you can see on the monitor that your child's oxygen saturations are going down. Where is the nurse? She's helping another patient. Why doesn't she drop everything she's doing to attend to your baby? Why would you even have a monitor if the nurse wasn't going to pay attention to it?!

As we said earlier, the nurse knows if the monitor is alarming danger or simply warning. And while you may believe your infant is the only baby in the room, there are usually fifteen other moms who feel the same way.

NICOLE'S TAKE:

No matter how many times I was warned, cautioned, advised (you name it) about the **monitors**, I became a slave to them as soon as I understood them. I seriously became glued to them; possibly because I couldn't see my son but also because I'm a control junkie and I believed if I could just master staying on top of them it would make all the difference. Trust me, it doesn't. Your infant is going to go on the course they are on. The monitors only help you understand what direction that course is—they don't provide the outcome.

DEB'S TAKE:

Despite the nurses telling me to look at Becky, I found myself continually drawn to the **monitor** in a very hypnotic state. Slowly I managed to stop doing that but it only started to become "routine" as we headed toward Discharge Day and prepped for a monitor to be at home.

You can watch the monitors and trust them, but only to a point. Monitors have been known to go on the fritz. Lead wires fall off. Trust that you will learn your infant's behavior and that you will begin to see physical signs of stress or distress that your baby is having. Upon returning home, most of you won't have monitors—and then it's imperative that you rely on looking at your baby to make sure he or she is okay.

NICOLE'S TAKE:

About a week after we had successfully **extubated** Nicholas, his T-com **monitor** went off the charts. He was **desatting**. We were frantic, trying to figure out how or why he was no longer able to oxygenate. Were they right? He simply would never get off the **vent**? His saturations stayed low, and the **neonatologist** had just rounded the corner, preparing to re-**intubate**. I was absolutely crushed as I glanced at Nicholas's bluish complexion. He had seemed so strong. They had already done a bunch of tests—with no results indicating that he was sick.

Suddenly one of the housekeepers realized Nicholas's **cannula** was not attached to his source of oxygen. The nurse, doctor, **RT**, me—we all were stumped, and ready to put Nicholas through re-intubation, only to find the lowest-tech issue in the world was the cause of his oxygenation problem. It was simply a disconnected tube. Human error.

Sometimes it pays to go the extra mile and consider everything, and not just what the monitors are telling you.

BREATHING ROOM

As difficult as it is for you to be a parent of a Preemie—often standing on the sidelines with anxiety, guilt, and confusion—it is often more difficult to be the actual Preemie. Preemies are born before their

time. In coming early, they then must suffer the consequences.

If your infant is lucky enough to be only a couple of weeks premature, they may have wanted to keep you on your toes; remind you they are about to take over your lives and just wanted to give you early notice.

But if your infant is born at 30 or 24 weeks, they are going to have a very rough time living outside the womb and they need all the help they can get. While the medical community has come up with the most amazing technological advances to save infants at earlier **gestational ages**, medicine, science, and technology can only do so much. Equally (and sometimes even more) important, are parents doing what they do best: loving their child, caring for them in every way they can and becoming their best advocate.

In doing so, it's very easy, and expected, for a parent to follow their gut instincts and snuggle, and smother their infant with love. Unfortunately, many Preemies and certainly most **Micro-Preemies** simply cannot endure too much of that kind of care. It's the most natural thing in the world for a parent to want to touch their child—they ache to do so—but you must remember that a Micro-Preemie's skin is like ash paper: acutely fine and sensitive. You must touch your baby as if it's a whisper. Their skin simply cannot take anything more.

It's difficult, but you have to give your Preemie the room to become a baby and do what they were supposed to do in utero: Grow.

MINIMAL STIMULATION REQUESTS

Minimum stimulation means exactly what it says: minimal contact with the infant. We know it seems harsh and cruel to keep a parent from their child, but it is exactly what they need for a period of time. Parents are agonized by the concept of minimum stimulation, but it truly is the only way for baby to grow strong and to have as few developmental issues as possible along the way.

No matter how advanced science and medical technology have become, they cannot replace the womb. There is nothing better or more effective for growing a fetus than to be in utero. So when a baby decides to come on the scene early, science had to find a way to most closely simulate an infant being in the womb.

Think of minimum stimulation as a darkened room. The door is shut, the lights are off, and sound is buffered from entering. Your infant needs the least amount of direct stimulation possible to maintain growth and health. Minimum stimulation has also proven over the years to positively affect the severity of developmental delay in these infants. What infant isn't going to respond negatively to harsh lights, constant juggling, and monitors going off all over the place? Even when it's impossible to keep it all out and away from baby (as any parent will soon see during a busy day on the NICU floor), the minimum stimulation provided for the baby is the best step in the right direction.

DEB'S TAKE:

Early on I was able to touch Becky in the **isolette** for a little bit at a time. A week later I was able to hold her. But mid-way through her NICU stay, Becky had a setback. As the staff did scans, ran blood work and ultimately gave her a blood **transfusion**, we were told to not touch her.

I was finally getting settled in and connecting with Becky more and more and then—WHAM!—no touch. It was awful. Wasn't I supposed to be the best thing for her?

THE SILENT CRY

One reason you may not be hearing your baby cry is that crying is hard work. Your Preemie may be too exhausted to even attempt to let out a big "Oh…I happen to be here" wail.

But another reason you may not be able to hear your baby cry is that it is impossible for **vented** babies to make noise when they cry. The tube inserted down their throat is wedged between the vocal chords, rendering them ineffective.

It may seem surreal and a little macabre to see your infant clearly screaming their heads off and not hearing anything, but understanding why your baby cannot cry will help ease the fear factor. While you may still find your child's silent cries disturbing, take heart in the fact that it's normal—normal for the NICU anyway.

NICOLE'S TAKE:

I would watch as Nicholas's mouth would open and knew that he was screaming. Nothing in the world made me feel more helpless than seeing him unable to cry, unable to let the world know what he was experiencing.

The second Nicholas was **extubated**, I realized that the little squeak that resembled a cartoon

voice was my son's first attempts at communication. For months his voice would croak, groan, and screech. It then became the soft soothing and gentle tone it is today. Now he uses his voice to sing…incessantly!

HOLDING/FEEDING YOUR BABY

Naturally it is every mother, and father's wish to hold and feed their baby. Again, this is a step you must take during the time that is safest for the baby and will not cause her any danger.

If your child is not hooked up to a **vent**, and is reasonably stable, there should be no reason that you cannot hold your baby as often as you can. Most hospitals have moved or are in the process of moving toward what is referred to as "**family centered care**" and realize the critical role a parent plays in the well-being of their infant. Holding your infant, or getting some **kangaroo** time in (*see* **A-Z: Kangaroo Care**, *page 56.*) where you hold your infant upon your chest and bond with him, is not only important for you but for baby as well. Again, you can do this when the baby is stable.

Feeding your infant is a very individual matter. Please see if you are able to **breastfeed** your baby *(see* ***A-Z: Breastfeeding****, page 31.*). If you are unable to breastfeed and your baby is taking formula by bottle, again, it will be necessary to make sure your baby is stable and/or able to bottle feed.

Unlike most babies who learn to suck and swallow shortly after they are delivered, eating in the NICU can be a very challenging situation. If your infant is on the vent, she will not be able to breast feed or take a bottle and will have to be fed either via a **nasal gastric tube** and/or via **central IV line**.

When a baby is on the vent for any length of time, they will have an **occupational therapist** or feeding specialist work with your infant to make sure they learn to develop the **suck-swallow** skills so that your baby can feed without the danger of **aspiration**. The longer your infant is on a vent, the more difficult it usually becomes for them to learn these skills as their mouth muscles are strained by the vent tube in one way and are weak in another because they have not had to develop these skills.

Your **neonatologist**, nurse, and team will help you come to an understanding of when it is safest for your baby to learn to feed. If it's been after a long vent stint, this will be a time of great celebration.

DEB'S TAKE:

One of the hardest milestones Becky struggled with was feeding. She was getting my pumped breastmilk through the feeding tube and I felt proud. Yet, part of the way through the stay, they had us do the first bottle feed for her. Lo and behold there was a bottle of cow-based fortifier used along with my breast milk. Later, my daughter contracted **sepsis** and I now highly suspect that this was directly related to the cow-based fortifier.

For parents with babies 1,250 grams and lower, you have a better option than bovine-based (cow-based fortifier) and it is your right to ask for it. Ask for a human milk-based fortifier and be clear that you want only a 100% human milk-based fortifier for your child.

PreemieWorld has specific, free resources regarding advocating for an exclusive human-milk diet for your child at these two links: PreemieWorld's "Special Edition" on an Exclusive Human Milk Diet: ***http://preemie.us/HumanMilkPW*** and Helping My Tiny Baby Thrive: ***https://preemie.us/ActionPlan***.

VENTILATOR

Ventilators are the machines that help your baby to breathe. The ventilators for us were simply the most amazing and magical machines science had ever invented. Because of these machines, so many of the smaller Preemies are able to survive. There are a plethora of machines and an equal number of ways to tweak these machines to optimize your infant's breathing and diminish side effects.

Remember that vented Preemies often already have inflamed and injured lungs. Even though the ventilator is a life saving device, it too can cause damage to the lungs if the pressure and size of the breaths are not adjusted correctly to your individual baby's needs.

On the vent machine monitors you may see some strange visuals appearing as a semi-triangular graphic and then disappearing. That image is not only a graphic of your child's very breath, but by dialing little knobs on these sophisticated ventilators the neonatologist can change not only the shape of the way your baby breathes in and out, but also the pressures with which they do by making minor changes to the PEEP and PIP. These are two acronyms you may hear a lot if your child is on a vent and here is **primary nurse** Becky Harrington's explanation for moms:

PIP is peak inspiratory pressure: this is the amount of pressure that is needed to "pop" open the baby's lungs during inspiration. (Normal PIP 15-22.)
PEEP is peak end respiratory pressure: the amount of pressure needed to keep the lungs from collapsing during/after expiration. (Normal PEEP 4-7.)

MAP is mean airway pressure: the number in between PIP and PEEP (you mostly hear people talking about that on the High Frequency Ventilators—HFV—the Oscillator or HFOV or Jet HFJV (you know—the loud ones that make their little bodies jiggle) are examples of HFV.

NICOLE'S TAKE:

For Mother's Day I receive the most awesome present: Jovan, honorary uncle to Nicholas and head **RT**, changes Nicholas's moustache, and for a few seconds I get to see my son's face. I'm truly awed by this experience. It strikes me that while I know Nicholas in a way that is more complete than almost anyone in my life, I really have very little clue as to what he looks like.

"There is no book on your baby. No research. No data we're going to tell you because we don't know."

-Dr. Richard Krueger,
Neonatologist to Nicholas

By delicately finessing the lengths of inhalation and exhalation, the measurements and shapes of tidal volumes, and the PIPS & PEEPS, the **neonatologists** and **respiratory therapists** do their very best to facilitate your infant's breathing.

Besides the obviously painful drawbacks to having a baby on a **ventilator**, especially if they have been on one since they were born, is the one that anguishes a parent—and that is that you are unable to see your infant's beautiful face.

THE MICRO-PREEMIE:

Though part of the general NICU population, the **Micro-Preemie** lives in its own special sub-category. During the time Nicholas was born, they didn't even run statistics for infants under 500 grams. They literally had no literature or outcomes, beyond the obvious negative ones, since there were so few infants in this category who survived.

preemieworld

During the time we were at the NICU, we saw many infants born between 500 and 750 **grams**. And they all had hellish courses. The unfortunate reality about the X-Micro Preemie (Extra-Micro-Preemie) is that their birth weight truly works against them. You may wonder: how small can medicine become? Yes, a microscopic chip can hold millions of pieces of information. However, when you try to translate the smallness of a human being to that level, it seems literally impossible for adult-sized hands to handle and care for an infant the size of a bird or a frog.

Many of the infants that are born "too **small for gestational age**" at these low birth weights are actually in a more developed gestational week. Nicholas should have been double his weight at 25½ weeks. Considering that these infants have scraped through to survive in utero—even with whatever complications are facing them—many of them come out "fighting strong" so your infant—even though very tiny—may actually have a better chance of survival because they are more developed if they fall into the category of "small for gestational age."

You will learn the will to survive is extraordinarily humbling in these circumstances, and as most of Nicholas's doctors will attest, they gave him zero chance of surviving his particular circumstances.

Meager as they are, the statistics give a spread of 10-80% chance of survival for Micro Preemies depending on their gestational week and birth weights. The statistics for a baby born at 23 weeks are harsher with only a 10% chance of survival at best.

When Nicholas was born as one of the few "under 500 grammers" born in the NICU, they told us they could only count on one hand how many had survived in the past 10 years. The reason for such a low survival rate is that there are so many systems inside the baby that are at risk: **brain bleeds**, underdeveloped neurological systems, intestines, and digestive systems (which lead to a high risk of **NEC/ Necrotizing Entercolotis**). All are on the **vent** and have lung problems, all run a very high risk of infection which they are too small to fight off, and all of this is while still living at the hospital. It does not begin to address the issues these kids will face when they get home and—often—have lifelong challenges from being so premature.

When you are in the NICU bay, you are bound to find yourself near a Micro-Preemie or even an X-Micro-Preemie. If you can remember that most of these kids are facing serious medical challenges, you will know how to deal with the parents who live by their **isolettes** and understand why they always seemed stressed out—if not a bit crazy.

MULTIPLES

Having one Preemie in the NICU is tough—imagine two or three or even more. While a number of these moms-to-be are well-educated in the ways of the NICU prior to delivery, they are still shell-shocked with double, triple or more of the stress. One of the keys to successful parenting of multiples is to be able to connect with other families of this type for years to come. Check out three resources for support in the next column.

Many NICUs may be **family-centered** in their care, but many also have equally stringent **HIPAA** (privacy) rules. These rules dictate that you give other families privacy, especially when it comes to staring at the babies and talking to other families. Ask your Charge Nurse what the rules are and if it is possible for you to connect with any other parents in the unit. Also, see if your hospital or local community has a Preemie support group. There is a worldwide listing on ***www.PreemieWorld.com.***

- ***Twinslist.org:***

This website has a large list of multiples related organizations across the world.

- ***RaisingMultiples.org:***

Over 30 years in service, support forums, local groups nationwide and around the world as well as a regular edition of Supertwins Magazine, Mothers of Supertwins (MOST) helps moms cope with the daily challenges of multiples parenting, both in high-risk pregnancy, the NICU and beyond.

- ***MultiplesofAmerica.org:***

Multiples of America aka National Organization of Mothers of Twins Clubs is a non-profit devoted to supporting and educating new and existing parents of multiples with clubs set up across the United States. It is a membership organization but provides lots of resources and opportunities to its members.

V.

PREEMIE PARENT = ADVOCATE

YOUR NEW ROLE AS A PREEMIE PARENT

We know you were set on being just the kind of parent your parents were (or perhaps the exact opposite). You probably had a vision of what parenting was going to be like. Or, perhaps, you had no clue. In any case, your role as a Preemie parent is quite different than anything you ever could have expected.

To start with, you're in the hospital, often in a medically challenging and even critical situation. Prepare yourself not only to deal with the premature birth of your infant, but also to be expected to make decisions to best help him or her. This means making the best medical decisions for your child in a world where you have had no orientation. Do you need to have a medical degree? No, but it helps to understand the medical terminology tossed around like Ancient Greek.

As you stand helplessly by an **isolette** or open crib, not allowed to touch your infant without the permission of a doctor or nurse, you'll begin to wonder what your role is. Being your baby's advocate is going to be at the top of the list.

HELPING YOUR PREEMIE THRIVE

Your infant may be on a **vent**, stuck to leads, hooked up to wires and **monitors**. He's untouchable. She's invisible in the surrounding supplies and equipment. How do you help him best to survive? How can you get her out of the hospital? How do you become the parent you have always wanted to be?

Listen. Listen carefully to your doctors. Especially listen to the nurses—they are your first and best line of defense and connection to your child. Doctors may have all the medical knowledge in the world, and certainly specialists will have the critical information only they can provide, but your nurse will be bed/**isolette**-side twelve hours a day (or night) and will be the first to better understand your baby.

Take in what you can and ask questions. Ask as many questions as you need to understand what is happening in this new environment. As soon as you get your feet wet and are ready to dive in, it's time to become your baby's advocate. Assume this role with confidence and it will dra-

matically help your child's course in the NICU. There may be a lot going on with your baby from which you feel excluded, but there is also a lot that you can do to help your baby.

When Nicole was looking for a resource guide to help her navigate these waters, she discovered several resource materials out there that gave the parents a free pass, letting them off the hook. Maybe it's a kinder, gentler thing to do (and she suspects it helps to sell more copies). These books suggest that it's okay to "just be a parent"—after all, that's all you were meant to be—and that the medical team should be solely responsible for your baby's other needs. While that hints at the correct order of things you will find that, in reality, your involvement in making medical decisions is demanded.

BEING AN ADVOCATE FOR YOUR BABY

Sure, the doctor may explain things to you in layman's terms. Perhaps, however, your doctor enjoys the fact that you are at her mercy. Or maybe he will spend arduous hours training you as though you were one of his residents. Regardless of what extreme you face, the important thing is that you truly understand the challenges your infant faces so that you can make the best decision for his or her well-being.

You'll note that we said "best" and not "right" decision—it helps not to think about making the "right" or "wrong" choice. The guilt you may feel when you watch your baby endure dozens of heel pokes or X-rays will be a burden not easily dismissed as the days roll into weeks. Some may see these tests and treatments as black-and-white, right or wrong, but you will know that these are the best calls to get your baby on the healthy track.

We have no desire to put undue pressure on those who feel that they simply cannot understand medical jargon. You aren't expected to be a doctor, but your baby expects you to be as informed as you can be to help them. Bond with a fellow Preemie mom or dad to work through the *medical-ese* together. Talk to your nurses. Read the **A to Z** section of this book as often as you need to.

THE ADVOCATE: YOU ARE THE DIRECT LINK BETWEEN MEDICINE AND MIRACLE

Ask for things. Request them. Expect them. Anything that you ask for (within reason and promising benefits, of course) should be accommodated. Discuss beginning **kangaroo care**. While it may be a bit of a juggle (especially if your infant is on a vent), the nurses and respiratory therapists are there to assist you. If your schedule permits, ask to **round with the doctors**. Some of them may agree, some may decline due to privacy issues. If they allow you to round, ask questions so that you may understand what's going on.

Ask for things that make sense. Many nurses have grown calloused by the repetition of what they do and it is possible that one may not handle your child with the all-important gentle care. If this (or anything else in this vein) happens, speak to a charge nurse and ask to have someone else put in charge of your baby. You are the customer and you are paying the bill. Even at a teaching hospital run by your county, you should be considered "always right."

ADVOCATING FOR YOURSELF

The sooner you realize that taking care of yourself will help your child, the better off you will be. This is not to suggest that you become a pain-in-the-butt parent that no one wants to work with, but it is important that the medical staff know that you are a force to be reckoned with. You are not to be "handled"—the hospital should understand that you are taking your job as advocate seriously. You are aware that this is a medicine about which you know nothing. You only want what is best for your child, but you also expect to be kept well-informed of all important changes in your child's medical status. You expect to be treated as a member of the team.

As the doctors realize that they can rely on you to be a level-headed person trying to do what is best for your newborn, they will soon respect you and want your involvement. Indeed, some may begin to turn to you for your input. In the end, no one should know your child better than you. And that's a great way to bond with your primary nurses ("A mom who's a pain in the butt saves *my* butt," one said).

- Do you have a parent orientation or welcome packet?
- Where are the restrooms?
- Where are the lactation rooms?
- Where is the hospital café (the one with the good coffee)?

- Where do I park? How do I obtain a weekly/monthly parking permit for long term stays? Is there is a point in the long-term stay where parking is free?
- Can I have a map of the hospital layout?
- Where is the nearest ATM, bank, pharmacy, gift store, newsstand, and Starbucks?
- Where are the vending machines? What coinage/paper do they take?
- Do you have a microwave?
- Is there an on-site Ronald McDonald House or other type of arrangement for families driving in long distance that may not be able to afford a hotel room?

NOTES:

____

____

____

____

____

Paperwork and Organization

You may feel as if you are being thrown a huge curve ball on the organization front. Not to fear, there are some simple ways to organize things on the paperwork.

- Have someone get you a practical baby shower gift of an expandable file, a medium-sized binder with a package of divider pages, a small steno pad, a student-type assignment calendar, and a package of ballpoint pens.
- In each section of the expandable file, start creating the sections such as "Hospital" and "NICU" to start off. This is a great place to put your paperwork from the variety of professionals you will be working with.
- The steno pad is useful for making notes and sticking them into the file. It can be used to create "to-do" lists, questions to ask the doctor when meeting, and even the ongoing "to-do" list for your Team Captain to spread out among those fabulous volunteers.
- The calendar is for you to keep track of your schedule while on the run if you don't have a calendar that you already use on your phone or other electronic device.
- Why so many pens? Pens disappear. It's that simple.
- The binder is for all insurance, **Medicaid**, and **SSI** items that you

receive now and in the future. Use the divider pages to set up and separate out everything.

- Take the expandable file with you to the NICU while the binder stays at home.
- On the home front you can also create some organization so as to make getting out of the house and getting to and from the hospital less chaotic.
- Get some water bottles (another great baby shower gift) and fill them several at a time so you can just grab and go, keeping healthy and hydrated without resorting to spending money at the hospital.
- Create a bunch of "snack bags" to create healthy snacks that you don't have to buy at the hospital or think about making every day. And if someone were willing to shop for these items and set them up for you, again another great and practical baby shower gift.
- Set up a special bag as your "car bag" everything you might need while there—tissues, a change of clothes, a sweatshirt or sweater, travel-sized items such as a face cleanser, toothbrush, toothpaste, and deodorant. Entertainment items could include a library book, a magazine, or a puzzle book. This bag would live in your car and come into the hospital with you as needed. Put a spring clip to the front of the bag to keep reminder notes and other items front and center on your attention as needed.
- Set up a "NICU bag" with tissues, a library book or magazine, your camera, breast pumping supplies, your snack bags, and bottles of water. This bag will be your go-to bag while in the NICU and it can stay in your assigned locker. Like the "car bag" use a spring clip on the front of the bag to attach important items in central focus.
- If your hospital does not allow cell phone usage or you do not have a cell phone, consider asking for yet another practical baby shower gift, a phone card.
- And while you are at it, consider asking for gift cards for local restaurants for days where the "snack bags" won't suffice.

"PAPERWORK: That which is handed to you at every conceivable, inconvenient moment possible."

-Nicole Conn

NICOLE'S TAKE

In the hours that you wait to see your son or daughter, you may dream of a paperless hospital. When I realized that day-dream was never going to happen, I thought up a solution—a position for every hospital with a **Level III NICU**. It would be a parent/hospital liaison and their job would be to accommodate every thing a parent needed the first week of their hospital stay. This is of course for parents who have either a critically ill infant or an infant who will easily be there for months, mind you.

I remember on day four after I had been utterly deprived of anything looking like two hours of sleep in a row, I asked about how to get a parking permit. The receptionist told me I had to go over to the south tower. (tower? I suddenly felt a medieval chill). I went over there only to find out—No!-—I would not get the parking permit—this place was only where I initiated the paperwork for the parking pass. Then I had to actually go to another building where I would get a receipt to go to yet another building where I could get the permit. I needed to get there by five o'clock, and I had to show several pieces of ID but first I had to go to the admissions office to get proof that my son even existed in this hospital.

I went straight to the bathroom and cried. I simply couldn't handle it. It was too much information on a brain in complete meltdown mode.

Here's what this hospital/parent liaison would do: They'd ask you if you needed coffee, even if they probably saw you with the seventh cup of the day. Perhaps they'd suggest something without caffeine. Had you eaten yet? They could show you the way to the cafeteria. And after they took you by the hand and walked you there, they would give you a little PDF map they had created to alert you to all CRITICAL SPOTS for parents with a legend simple enough for a five year old to follow. This map would alert you to the nearest restrooms, the coffee shop, the hospital cafeteria, the nearest vending machines, toiletries, outlying banks, and dry-cleaners.

Ahhh, well, it was a nice dream while it lasted (but you could help another mom by filling this role when you've been around a while.)!

A SPECIAL NOTE FOR DADS:

Dads definitely tend to get the short end of the stick when it comes to all things NICU. While the mother feels left out of the parenting experience, the dads feel completely ignored and end up dealing with so much of the outside world chaos instead. While we know the NICUs don't intend to make this occur, it does. Dads hear us loud and clear: You are very important to the well-being of mom and baby during this time so come to the NICU whenever humanly possible. And here are some tips of things you can do on your own to bond with your child:

Gregg with Preemie-sized Shirt
Photo Credit: Deb Discenza

Gregg holding Becky
Photo Credit: Deb Discenza

- Read to your baby (yes, the baby knows your voice)
- Touch your baby when given touch time
- Hold your baby whenever allowed
- Do kangaroo care with your baby (warning: Preemies grab chest hair!)
- Change a Diaper
- Sing or hum a song to your baby
- Just say your baby's name and say hello
- Help decorate the incubator or surrounding area as allowed by NICU rules
- When bath time comes along, bathe your baby

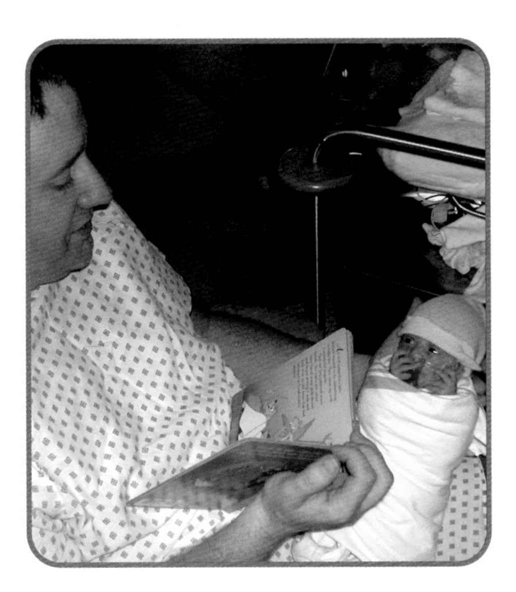

Gregg reading to Becky
Photo Credit: Deb Discenza

Life is definitely stressful for a couple that has a baby in the NICU and it is a time that can change a relationship forever. Some tips on keeping your relationship solid can include:

Family picture
Photo Credit: Gregg Discenza

- Sitting with the baby together quietly.
- Taking a family photo (ask a nurse for help with this, they do this all the time. Just make sure you are not interrupting their workload at the moment).
- Get outside and breathe some fresh air together and go for a short walk.
- Sit down outside and talk about something unrelated to the NICU that makes you both happy.
- Try to give yourselves a break on old arguments. You have enough to deal with at the moment.
- Stand together as a united front when handling family and friends and the inappropriate comments.
- Help mom unburden her emotions. If she needs to cry, let her cry. You need to do nothing but hold her. And it is okay for you to cry as well. You have been dealt a hard blow, too. Make sure that any emotions you are both working through are watched. Post-Partum Depression (PPD) is common with new mothers and especially parents of special needs babies. They are also at risk for Post-Traumatic Stress Disorder (PTSD) *(see **The Importance of Self-Care**, page 158 and 159)*.

- Provide little acts of kindness such as helping mom with heavy equipment like carrying the rented breast pump to and from places. Or help her postpartum rest a bit more by offering to get the car and pull it up to an entrance instead of her having to walk the extra distance to the parking lot. Or bring her a bottle of water from a vending machine or the cafeteria prior to her going to the breast pumping room (she'll need it and she'll thank you wholeheartedly!).
- Try to build the landscape of your future together: talk about what you can do to help prepare the nursery or what your plans are for making the homecoming special and more.
- Get that cigar—you deserve it (just don't bring it into the NICU)!

ADVOCATING FOR NUTRITION

One area in specific that both parents should advocate for in the NICU is their baby's nutrition. As you will read in the glossary definitions on **breastfeeding** and **fortification**, nutrition is not always as straightforward as one would think.

Breastfeeding is not always possible with Preemie Moms. Although Mom's milk is definitely the best thing for your baby, the stress, the early birth all play into affecting milk production. If it doesn't work out, you tried and that is key.

The reality is, **fortification** is going to happen anyway with these small preemies. Breastmilk only provides so many nutrients and the team is trying to get as many into your baby as possible in order to promote appropriate growth and weight gain.

Many NICUs will resort to cow-based fortification. For decades it was the way to go. But not anymore. For preemies under 1,250 grams you do have choices, you do have a say and you do have rights.

Make it clear that you want your baby to receive Mom's milk and if needed, pasteurized donor milk and a 100% human milk-based fortifier. Even if they don't have it in stock, they can order it. It is up to you to ask and to make clear your preference.

Download the Exclusive Human Milk Diet guide: ***https://preemie.us/HumanMilkPW*** and also the Helping My Tiny Baby Thrive action plan: ***https://preemie.us/ActionPlan***

Click here to provide a Letter of Medical Necessity to give to your provider in order to apply for insurance coverage: ***https://preemie.us/MedicalNecessityLetter***

VI.

THE DOCTOR, NURSES, & YOU

YOUR ROLE IN THE BERMUDA TRIANGLE

A fascinating dynamic exists in the NICU where the medical staff really must play "mommy" until a baby is well enough for the mother to have much contact. Indeed, mom also has to be well enough from labor and delivery to play that role herself.

For the doctor and nurse to be the first mom, the parent and staff are (on some level) pitted against another. A mother's natural instinct is to want to care for her baby. As for doctors, "do no harm" is a guiding mantra. In cases where NICU staff must protect a seriously ill infant from a mother who is unable or incapable of taking care of their own baby, these instincts can clash.

So you ask yourself, "Am I still the mom/dad?" They call you mom, but may act as though you don't exist. Was that a neonatologist or a respiratory therapist who just did that strange thing to my infant? Doctor who? What was that nurse's name?

Your baby has a team, one that you should get to know ASAP. Knowing these people—and remembering that you are an integral party of the team—is the all-important first step.

It's rather like a shotgun wedding!—You're forced into this strange dynamic of caring for your baby with these people you don't even know (but must trust). You'll find some members of the medical staff wonderful, engaging, and willing to hold your hand through this process. Yet in what feels like speed-dating, you're also forced to meet and interact with an endless number of different people from the doctors to the nurses to the respiratory therapists to the social workers to the parent liaisons, etc. You may not be sure how you fit into the whole scheme of things, whom you can trust, and whether what that person just said is actually best for your baby.

Erratic and unsettling though it may be, you can still figure out how to maintain a sense of balance and harmony in all of this:

NICU ORGANIZATIONAL CHART

NICU Director or Medical Director: The managerial head of the NICU.

Neonatologists: A doctor with training in the NICU environment who oversees the medical teams who care for newborns. From the beginning of medical school, it takes a minimum of 10 years of training to become a neonatologist.

Neonatal Nurse Practitioners (NNPs): A nurse that has had additional training in the field of neonatology and has the ability to order tests and prescribe medications. NNPs usually at least have a master's degree.

Fellow: Attending physician in training that has already completed a pediatric residency and is a board certified pediatrician. Fellowships typically require an additional 3 years of training in a specialized field of medicine.

Intern: A first-year resident; just graduated medical school.

Resident: Completed first year or two of three years of residency.

Charge Nurse: The nurse in charge of the nurses on the shift. This individual usually makes assignments for patient care and should be consulted if any concerns arise regarding staffing on a shift.

Nurse Director/Nurse Manager: A nurse who has had extra training in the NICU and is in a managerial position. This Nurse Director/Manager often sets NICU policy and oversees NICU management with the neonatologist.

Neonatal Nurse: Additional training after being a bedside NICU nurse for several years. This nurse now is concentrating on care of the newborn infant.

Nurse/NICU Nurse/RN: Practice independently; registered with the RN state board.

Licensed Vocational Nurse (LVN)/ (Licensed Practical Nurse (LPN): Licensed positions that require 1-2 years of education/training and are overseen by an RN.

Respiratory Therapists (or RT): Therapists who understand the mechanics of the **ventilator** and how and what the infant requires for care of lung-related problems.

Developmental Specialists (PT, OT, Speech Therapist): In the NICU these specialists help your baby with various motor functions such as feeding and **suck-swallow** organization (Speech Therapist) daily living issues (**Occupational Therapist** or **OT**), and muscle tone (**Physical Therapist** or **PT**).

Pharmacist: Oversees and works with the MD/NNP to make sure they are ordering the proper medications and dosages for the baby. Also mixes TPN and parenteral solutions, as well as oversees the stocking of formulas.

Dietician/Nutritionist: This specialist helps make sure the MD/NNP is giving the appropriate nutritional needs in **TPN** and formula for maximum weight gain.

Lactation Consultant: Provides help for the mother with **breastfeeding** and breast pumping needs.

Social Workers: Social Workers are there to help you navigate resources that you need and connect you with emotional support help such as preemie support groups, other families, and therapists.

Follow-Up Developmental Clinic: The clinic that your child may or may not be qualified for in terms of developmental assessment at certain points within the first few years after the NICU stay. This team consists mainly of therapists but may include other specialists as well.

Chaplain: A person who may be of a particular faith or of an interfaith manner that can be of use to you for comfort and support when needed.

Transport Service Staff: Staff who handle the transport of your baby to another hospital should he need specialized care only available at another hospital.

NICU Specialists

- ***Audiology*** (hearing issues)
- ***Cardiology*** (heart issues)
- ***Cardiovascular Surgery*** (heart surgery)
- ***Craniofacial/Plastic Surgery***
- ***Endocrinology*** (hormonal issues)
- ***Gastroenterology*** (digestion matters, NGT/GT)
- ***Genetics/Metabolic diseases*** (genetic counseling)
- ***Hematology/Oncology*** (blood issues/tumor issues)
- ***Infectious Diseases*** (infection issues)
- ***Nephrology*** (kidney issues)
- ***Neurology/Neurosurgery*** (brain and spinal issues)
- ***Ophthalmology*** (eye issues)
- ***Orthopedics*** (bone/skeletal issues)
- ***Pediatric Intensive Care*** (later care of older infants)
- ***Pediatric Urology*** (bladder issues)
- ***Pulmonology*** (lung issues)
- ***Radiology*** (x-rays and imaging studies—CT, Ultrasounds, MRI)
- ***Thoracic and Abdominal Surgery*** (surgery in the thoracic and abdominal areas)

NICOLE'S TAKE:

I found it strange that the babies are all called by their last name and the moms are all referred to as "mom." I wonder if this is an intentional way to keep us all at bay. I knew it probably made sense, but on some level I felt it was so impersonal. And every time anyone said "mom" all our heads would swivel in unison. Try not to take this personally. Remember that your NICU will care for dozens of babies a month and there is no way to remember everyone's name.

DOCTORS, NURSES, AND YOU

"We are haunted by the ghosts of our successes."

-Dr. Richard Krueger,
Nicholas's Primary Neonatologist

The Doctors

Just as all patients are unique, so too are doctors. Though you'll meet a few with major Messiah Complexes, most understand that being a doctor does not make them God. Many will be the first to tell you that it is a problem with the profession: doctors hold life and death in their hands, and it cannot help but affect them.

Most doctors—at least **neonatologists**—are in the profession because they excel at commitment, devotion, and dedication. You cannot take anything lightly in this line of medicine, and these men and women on the front lines of this brave new science are doggedly trying to determine what will best work for your infant.

Do their bedside manners leave something to be desired? Quite often, yes. You may love the crazy maverick that will do what no other doctor can or will. But between him and the eleven other neonatologists at your baby's bedside, it is nerve-wracking to watch the face-off between young doctors willing to try anything and those stuck in the old school where mothers and fathers bowed to their benevolent powers. It's nerve-wracking for these people as well.

The concept of **family centered care** is quite new; many hospitals have yet to implement it. This means you may be dealing with a doctor who wants to help you understand everything being done to help your infant or you may have a doctor who wants you to go away. Remember that it is your right and duty as your baby's advocate to voice your intent of being involved with their treatment and welfare.

You may have moments when you do not see eye-to-eye. You may go through hell with the doctor to whom you're closest. It could be a painful experience for both; it could be an experience that lasts beyond Discharge Day. At the end of the day, however, they're human just like you. They have their own defenses, denials, and confidence issues.

"You were a great advocate for your son. You were also a pain in the ass."

-Dr. Richard Krueger,
Nicholas's Primary Neonatologist

NICOLE'S TAKE:

The doctor who got my son off of the **vent** and I had a hell of a rough time. Through the six months we lived on the floor, he and I got into yelling matches that actually cleared the floor. And even though his approach was wildly maverick, he gave Nicholas and I the gift of getting my son off the vent.

A month after that, his aggressive approach on Nicholas's feeds drove me crazy, and indeed did not work. More yelling and arguing. A "dispute" meeting was called with the Chief of Staff in the NICU along with all of the players who were called into to "handle me" and the situation. When I walked into the room, he happened to be the only one there and I sat stiffly waiting for the others. He turned to me so sweetly and said, "It must be hell for you trying to take care of your son when we are all telling you different things."

It was strange. He was the doctor with whom I had the worst time, yet to whom I felt the closest. In the end he told me that the experience for him with me and Nicholas was the "most painful" he had ever encountered; not just because I was a pain in the butt for him, but because he could tell I was passionately advocating for my son and he wanted to help me and he and I simply couldn't see eye to eye at times. He's also the same doctor who came to visit my son a year later when Nicholas was deathly ill with an MRSA infection, and with tears in his eyes reflected on his affection for my son.

Other Doctors

You will also come into contact with many interns, residents, and fellows. The only reason you meet most of them is because they must do their rotation on the NICU. Very few plan to specialize in neonatal care except the fellows who are specifically there to specialize in neonatology. At times, this becomes difficult: in the order of the pecking system: nurses come after interns, **residents**, and **fellows**. Yet because they live, eat, and breathe the floor (many of them for years), it is quite clear they know far more than these newbies.

The Nurses

As difficult and as challenging as it may be to accept, your baby's first

"NICU Nurses have the biggest egos."
-Judy Ostheimer,
Primary Nurse to Nicholas

mom is going to be his nurse. Like us, you may be a high-maintenance mom and very concerned with your baby's well being. If you're like Nicole, you want to **round with the doctors** and understand all of the medical aspects surrounding your infant. The problem is that the nurse assigned to your infant is also his or her caregiver. At first, they must do all of the "mothering" until you learn how to perform such duties to the staff's satisfaction.

As parents, it's important to step back and take a look at the NICU from the nurse's perspective. How do they do those insane 12-hour shifts, often turning into 15-hour days with the paperwork and commutes? We only have our one infant (or multiples), which is certainly enough medical drama for any person. Nurses are scrambling to care for several families at once. If you ask them, they'll tell you that seeing a Preemie they've worked with for months on Discharge Day or returning year after year at NICU Reunions showing great progress gives them real satisfaction. But what about the stuff in between?

How do they deal with the infants who come early, some only making it for several days or weeks? What if there is nothing wrong with these children other than the fact that they are early? What if there are no **brain bleeds** but your infant becomes **septic** (as in Nicholas's case)? How do they keep both mom and baby from falling apart?

But the issues between mom and nurse are more than the gray division of labor on who's mom and who's nurse. In today's nursing world there is also a huge communication gap. For many of the nurses that will attend to your baby, English is a second language. We know that right now English probably feels like a second language to you as well. But seriously, this can cause huge issues in and of itself. If a language barrier is insurmountable, speak to the charge nurse.

I coo to my son "my sweet little monkey" having no idea that, for my Filipino nurse, this is an outrage. I insist to her it's an endearment. Hasn't she seen me wearing my Monkey George shirts? Or the mini Monkey George that's been in his isolette since Day 2? But apparently the damage has been done. She will never work with me again.

NICOLE'S TAKE:

I ask Agnis how she deals with what she went through the other day, but she only answers indirectly in her quiet, gentle manner. She tells me how the mother was brought in from L&D on a gurney to see her baby and hold him before the infant went into surgery early that morning. When the baby returned, I heard through another mother that his heart rate never really got much above 80. Apparently the parents were aware that too many things were wrong.

Agnis gets teary eyed. "It was so sad." She says in her slight lisp and very heavy Filipino accent. "But once I'm with father who doctors say de baby must be off the **vent**. De baby he won't make it they tell the father. So he struggle and struggle and then finally decide to take off the vent. He holding baby and…"

I'm about to lose it. She begins to giggle and I'm afraid the stress of her job has gotten to her, "…and de baby keep breathing. Den the baby live. He keep going and breathing and he continue on and now he two year old." I can't even imagine what that father and mother must have gone through. It must be the strangest sort of horrific relief.

"Once I'm with mother and she gets baby and it doesn't make it and the only one who help her is secretary. She crying. I crying and secretary…we all crying. Den I have to take baby wrapped to de morgue."

I see now that this is how Agnis deals. Things are light and happy or they are "so sad." I don't think she can afford to dwell on it much more than that.

"Yes…after Tuesday I go home and I see de baby face in my dreams."
Even in her broken English it is clear what she is saying. Anguish does not require interpretation.

ESTABLISHING A PRIMARY-CARE DOCTOR AND NURSE

It is one of the most unique and bizarre relationships. The nurse is often times your infant's first mom. They are the ones who handle, touch, feed, and care for your baby. Many of them have special certificates just for the handling of babies weighing less than 1000 **grams**. (They called it the "Cradle Club" at Cedars.) They are the conduit to your Preemie. They can make your life hell or sheer bliss.

After spending hours together, you will invariably form relationships with some of the nurses. It is critical if you find yourself in the situation of having a long hospital stay to find the best primary nurse for your baby as well as for yourself.

It's normal to want to connect and rely on someone who is your direct access immediately. But if you can, take time in choosing your primary. As with every other relationship in the world, some nurses start off with their best bed-side manner and end up being your worst enemy. Some may be very friendly and cheerful (and you need that optimism around you!), but they may not have the greatest nursing skills. Or you may get a nurse whom you feel is completely wrong for you and your infant who turns out to be a life-long friend.

NICOLE'S TAKE:

There is also the possibility that a nurse will become a mother not only to the baby, but to the parent of the baby. Judy Ostheimer became that for me. I so desperately needed a mother to tell me it was okay, or in Judy's case to snap one wise-crack after another at me. I called her "Granny Bear" because she always acted so cranky. She spent half the day giving me a hard time, the other half holding my hand. I seriously would not have made it without Judy, KJ, Stephanie, and (of course) Becky.

DEB'S TAKE:

Nurse Donna was a huge boost to my confidence as a new mom, especially when she taught me how to give my daughter her first bath. With my husband and my mother present and a movie camera whirring away, I was instructed to pull off Becky's leads to her **monitors**. As I peeled off each lead I found myself fascinated. With the first splash of the

water on Becky and her unhappy wail, I was suddenly aware that this was the first time I had ever held Becky—just Becky. No wires, no blankets, no diaper, no leads, nothing. And as I massaged her back with some soap her face turned to pure bliss. For me this was like a re-birth of sorts. I held my very naked daughter and washed her, and it was if I was transported into labor and delivery again and given a chance to hold her as a newborn.

One of our main **neonatologists**, now on his second rotation with Nicholas, has explained that morale is at an all-time low because of the nursing shortage and believes the nurses have become prima-donnas. If they don't like a patient or they think the parents are too demanding, they say they don't want to work in that situation.

"Excuse me," he mutters, disgruntled, "but a nurse can never say that a parent is too demanding in the NICU. The baby has no way to advocate for himself so the parent must be able to say whatever she needs to take care of her baby. This idea that a nurse can decide that a parent is demanding is intolerable."

WORKING WITH THE PROS AND CRAFTING A GREAT RELATIONSHIP

Finding the right balance not only between all these various doctors but also adding in the nurses makes it amazingly difficult to craft the role of being a patient parent, a good advocate, and simply a mom.

Here's the deal: We're all human. The doctor. The nurse. The mom. We hear the doctor say one thing and the nurse hears another. The nurses hear me say one thing, repeat something else to the doctor. If it turns out that we're all hearing different things, I won't let it go until resolution has been accomplished. That's our jobs as parents. They may think you are challenging their competency. Assure them that that is not the case and you just need to get to the bottom of the confusion to be your baby's best advocate.

ROUNDING WITH THE DOCTORS

You are separated from your baby by a plastic bin that may as well be the Iron Curtain or the Great Wall of China. You have no idea what you are doing in this surreal universe—a universe you didn't know existed until your baby was born. You haven't slept in days. You feel as if you are

in constant chaos and out of control. You feel as helpless as it gets.

The best way to decrease the feelings of helplessness is to shed some of the components over which we have no control. Gaining a sense of empowerment in this kind of situation will help you immensely. Gathering this new information and utilizing a combination of lay person's medicine and intuition will help you gain the confidence you need to see if you agree with the doctor and, if not, to make suggestions.

Rounding with the doctors may not be as easy as we suggest. There are natural barriers to entry here: How well one can grasp medical information and jargon, how emotionally spent you are, and how inclined you are to put one more thing on your plate. Let's not forget it also depends on how willing a doctor is to include your participation involved in rounding.

NICOLE'S TAKE:

For a time, Nicholas's **isolette** was right across from a professional couple who both worked from their home. The wife was one of those sunny Californians, her daughter a 29-weeker. She never caused any waves and seemed to be in a perpetual state of sunny disbelief: "Oh, you know—me and my luck."

One day she came in to find her daughter on a **ventilator**. I could overhear the couple complaining about the medicine dosages being completely wrong. I didn't want to impose but I went over to listen. I let them rant and kvetch about how things could so easily get screwed up. And we commiserated over the fact their daughter had to be put on a **vent** because she had caught what Nicholas had—hospital **pneumonia**. Since they both worked from the home, I suggested that one of them make a point of **rounding with the doctors**, or at least coming for shift change when the nurses reported out to one another. That way they could monitor the goings-on and stay on top of all the cracks into which human error sinks.

From that moment forward, the parents rounded every day until their daughter got off the vent. And then the mother returned to her suspension of disbelief. While I remained the high-maintenance mom on the floor, so many nurses told me, they'd rather have a mom like me that "saves their butt" over and over again than to get into a situation that everyone will later regret.

THE ROTATION SYSTEM

"You have to trust us," the head neonatologist said to us.

"Yeah, but which one of you?" I retorted.

Part of the NICU rollercoaster is the whiplash that comes from the rotation of doctors and nurses, both monthly and on weekends and evenings. It's extremely difficult for parents to volley between conservative and aggressive doctors, but in the world of high-stress, high-impact medicine a doctor can only handle so many emergencies, traumas, and all-nighters. The only way of handling such medicine is for doctors to leave the rotation system from time to time, although it does leave much to be desired in terms of continuity and creating a standard of care.

The disregard one doctor has for a colleague's plan of care can be mind-boggling. Even with the reporting out, it can take the new doctor a week to get up to speed on a complex patient and understand all of the specific idiosyncrasies. More likely than not, that doctor will then implement a new care plan that would just begin when rotation starts all over again. Part of this variability, though, to defend physicians, is that babies in the NICU really do change frequently in their needs. What may be appropriate one day may be completely wrong the next. This issue is often difficult for families to grasp and it looks like the doctors and nurses are all over the place.

Which begs the question: How can that not run the greatest risk of patient care not being at its optimum? The rotation system isn't going away. Shifts have to be covered and there is no other way to really cover them other than having some kind of rotation system. We all try in our heads to figure out a perfect resolution, but soon believe there isn't any. Mistakes happen, and they actually happen a lot more frequently than anyone cares to admit.

But you do have some power to work within the rotation system. Again, if you are able, **round with the doctors** and try to be there for one of the shift changes. You get an entire history of your baby's last 12 hours when one nurse reports out to another. Ask the nurses questions so you can feel like you understand the general conditions. If you can't be there, can your spouse? Mother? Best friend?

There is no quick fix to this system, but being there as much as you can and playing the role of advocate for your baby will be the best way you can deal with the musical chair care providers. We'll be the first

to tell you that this *is* a problem, but if you're aware of this being the one big contradiction to **continuity of care**, then you will be able to figure out the best resolution for you, your baby, and your particular situation.

THE SOCIAL WORKER

Like all other NICU relationships, finding the right social worker for you is about individuals and personalities, though the size of the hospital you're in will impact whether you actually have a choice. Some social workers may not be prepared to work with your case, others will be present and aware—a must for every social worker in this situation.

Build a great relationship with your social worker; if things aren't going well on the floor he or she can become your best friend. Request a change if you're not comfortable. Even though you may only see your social worker for weekly family meetings, they are always available to you. They are an integral part of the team. And the good ones make a world of difference.

HOUSEKEEPING, THE NUTRITIONIST, AND THE PHARMACIST

The NICU also features a cast of characters you may not necessarily see, but who are available to you at all times. Housekeeping is an interesting set of individuals who deserve your kindness and respect. They keep the place clean and running—and you want your NICU to be as organized as humanly possible. Introduce yourself and your infant to them. When you need an extra warming blanket, pillow, or diaper in the middle of the night, they, too, can be your best friend.

If your infant is having any feeding issues, another hugely important staff member is the nutritionist. Perhaps it's because food is life, but these folks are maniacal about making sure your infant is getting every doggone calorie they need on a daily basis. There will be days during rounds that the nutritionist will question the **neonatologist**, the surest reminder that getting your baby to gain weight is the major battle in the NICU. Besides being in your baby's corner food-wise, your nutritionist will also be able to talk you through the benefits of one formula over another. You may walk away numbed from all of the information, but at least you will know that there is someone who knows this stuff inside and out who is willing to help you find what's best for your baby.

Finally, if you feel like a broken record asking the nurses about the potential side effects of each drug prescribed for your baby, they will most likely direct you to the pharmacist. Putting so many medications in your infant's little body may be one of the most nerve-wracking parts of the NICU, but these pros will help you understand how each drug works, the side-effects that may present in your baby and how it is they work for your baby. They can also be a useful ally in suggesting an alternative medication to the neonatologist in case the side-effects your baby is experiencing seem too high a price for the cure.

PATIENT ADVOCACY

As we discussed in the last chapter, you have a new job as your baby's advocate. Every hospital has a patient advocate's office. Locate yours as soon as you can and know that it is there for you if you need it. You may be able to resolve most issues during your NICU stay with the staff straight-on, but if there is an issue that is not being resolved to your satisfaction, patient advocacy is there to help you.

"Look, when you've gone to medical school and done your fellowship, and then become a neonatologist, then you can argue with me about this stuff!"

-Reply to Nicole who had apparently asked one too many questions!

REMEMBER WHO'S PAYING THE BILL

No doctor should ever say these words to a mother. You do not have to be a doctor to discuss your son's medical condition. However, personalities clash. Depending on how sick your infant is, things can get very stressful between yourself and the medical staff—especially if you hold opposing views as to what's best for your baby.

One thing you always need to remember, bottom line, is that you are the customer. And, as the old adage goes, "The customer is always right."

We know the idea of you saying, "I'll just take my business elsewhere" is not only dramatic, but completely impractical. You can barely get through the day as it is and your infant is strung up on so much medical machinery that the last thing you can fathom is transferring to a different hospital. And it's very unlikely that things would ever get to the point that you would.

Remember that the hospital has an image to uphold, and that many derive a massive amount of revenues

from their NICUs. It is an exploding science, unfortunately with more and more babies on their way through those DO NOT ENTER doors. The hospital wants to create a wonderful and welcoming environment for all of its patients. More likely than not, your experience will be conveyed to the next Preemie Mom. The NICU will not want you walking around telling horror stories. If you do have problems, work with all of your resources to resolve them. Give your point of view, but also listen to others' opinions. You'll be surprised at some of the agreements that can be reached with a clear head and an objective discussion.

WAYS TO RESOLVE CONFLICT IN THE NICU

- **If possible, step away and breathe.** The NICU is a stressful place for everyone, so step out of the unit if you can and distract yourself with a walk or some deep breathing in a quiet place.
- **Write it down.** Sometimes the act of putting something down on paper (or in your phone or tablet can spark solutions.
- **Personality Fit.** Sometimes the nurse caring for your child is not a great fit for you and/or your child. See the Charge Nurse (this might also be the Nurse Manager or Nurse Director) and request a switch.
- **Contact the hospital's Patient Advocacy Department for help with the issue.** They do a great job of mediating difficult situations.
- **Ask for a second opinion.** If the team is telling you something that doesn't seem right to you, you do have the right to request a second opinion from within the unit or another unit.
- **Go to the top.** If the struggle has become too much and you feel the care is not appropriate, contact the Medical Director for the unit. This person oversees the entire NICU operation and can intervene to investigate, make changes, and with that, address your concerns.
- **When you have a meeting, bring at least one trusted person if not two.** This helps in a variety of ways. First, having at least another person there to back up your concerns lends weight to the issue. Second, having another person there to help point out details that you might forget in the heat of the moment. Third, that extra person can be a note taker for you for the meeting. With a stressful meeting you may not recall the details later on so that extra pair of eyes and ears is worth the effort.

VII.

COPING WITH EMOTIONS

THEY ARE ALL VALID

So how many times have you heard the term "rollercoaster" applied to your stay? 10? 50? 100? The reason it's so overused is because it really is the best term to describe the many ups and downs that can take place during one week, one day, or one hour. Emotional wreck and smiling mom are both "correct" responses. It's okay to freak out one minute and be calm the next. We refer to this as the "new" normal, and we have all been there, done that, and got the T-shirt.

DEB'S TAKE:

Years before Becky's birth, I had heard from another mother that the nurses and Child Protective Services could take away your baby if you vocally said you couldn't handle taking care of him or her. That scared the daylights out of me. So when Becky was born, while I wanted to weep bedside, I held it all in and played the Smiling Mom. I didn't know that it was okay for me to cry. I was too terrified. I went home and bawled every night sitting in front of my computer as I looked at my daughter's pictures and played a super-dramatic movie of her that my father-in-law had made.

You will discover in short order that being on the rollercoaster is simply a matter of life in the NICU. It's like breathing. And just as quickly as a breath comes and goes, you can experience something very drastic to something wonderful and vice versa.

NICOLE'S TAKE:

Within the first twenty-four hours I hear the term "roller-coaster" about a hundred times. If I hear the term one more time, I will scream. First of all it is an erroneous term. The rapid descents into illness are much more terrifying than the 215-foot drop at Magic Mountain. The ride is not a thrill of lifetime, it is terror heaped upon anxiety. The term is apt only in so far as the inability to regain equilibrium and the great desire to vomit on a daily basis. Nicholas's good moments become a ticking time-bomb. It is only a matter of seconds before the next event; bowel perforations, renal failures, collapsed lungs. I wish this were less of a rollercoaster and more of a merry-go-round.

HELPLESSNESS AND HOPELESSNESS

Events like **coding** are, unfortunately, the norm for many who live in the NICU. But how do you make it through these kinds of critical events? One **code** is almost more than a parent can bear, how do you stand by the **isolette** day after day, watching an infant who might not just be ill but relentlessly close to death? Helplessness and hopelessness overwhelm parents during this kind of tenure. Believe it or not, there are some things that you can do to mitigate the events over which you have no control.

Certainly another huge dose of helplessness comes from the overwhelming issues of stress, fatigue, and the emotional drain on your stamina, patience, and nerves. Not to mention being utterly sleep deprived distorts anyone's best judgment. If you have just undergone a horrendous delivery and you're still feeling sore and medicated, the best thing you can do is ask your spouse, partner, or best friend stand in for you to help navigate in the early days. It's also incredibly daunting to find yourself in this new sci-fi world and easy to be intimidated by the extent of new information you will face. You probably want nothing more than to crawl under a rock and escape. But make no mistake—there may be one or many times you will be asked to participate in making decisions—life and death decisions and it's important that you feel equipped to do so.

If at any time you feel helpless; take a peek at your infant in the **isolette**. It will make you realize just how much in control of your universe you are. While the odds may not look good, and it is doctor's job to make dire predictions, it's your job to hold onto hope.

preemieworld

NICOLE'S TAKE:

Months after we left the hospital, I discovered that the entire staff thought I had lost it when we celebrated Nicholas's first week of life with party hats and little cupcakes. I was the crazy mom who believed her **Micro-Preemie** was going to make it out of the hospital alive. All my primary nurses explained later on that they were simply humoring us at that time. After the fact this seemed so terrible, that the staff would feel they had to go along with a terrible charade so the crazy mother doesn't lose it. But in the end, I'm glad they played along. If I didn't feel like I had their support I would have been even worse off.

DEB'S TAKE:

What Helped Me Cope:

- Pumping breast milk (did wonders for my hormones)
- Kangarooing with Becky on a regular basis
- Talking with my husband
- Talking with a professional and understanding that my emotions were normal considering the situation at hand

As you live through the next few days and weeks, find a way to travel beyond your own pain, horror, and confusion. Try to reframe the landscape in which you have found yourself. Yes, you now belong to this unique club you didn't even want to join, but you have also been blessed with an opportunity to learn about things you would never have been exposed to. To feel the nascent souls passing through in a world that is as riveting as it is surreal—as anxiety-inducing as it is awe-inspiring.

The NICU can be the setting for one's most horrific nightmare, but it is also the place filled with unbelievable courage, intractable faith, and unyielding hope. If there ever was a venue for one's spiritual awakening, this is it. The questions each parent faces are the essence of motherhood and fatherhood. Parenthood here is not about buying the right pram, but about finding the right prayer. Motherhood is not about the suckling of a baby to her breast, but a queasy hope that one might hold her baby at all. Doing what is best for your baby is a haunting, relentless question: At what price life?

NICOLE'S TAKE:

During my tenure at the hospital, I found to my horror that certain babies on **ventilators** had simply become abandoned to become wards of the state. The nurses explained that it is not unusual for some parents, who simply cannot "deal" with seeing their infant on a ventilator. It's not a pleasant sight to be sure. But as unpleasant as it is for us to look at, it's even more difficult for the infant who is plucked before their time from the safety and warmth of a womb, plopped into a sterile **isolette** with a tube thrust down her throat so that she may be able to breathe. That to me is the epitome of helplessness—a Preemie infant who is left to fend for herself.

I lived by a law in the NICU, it was a mantra I had to apply daily: If Nicholas can go through it, I can damn well stand there and hold his hand while he's doing so.

I don't mean to be harsh here. And I know everyone has their own individual fear factor, but the fact is, as much as you may not have wanted this to happen to you, your infant wants it even less.

That's the end of my tough love rant.

Now, there are a million reasons to feel helpless. It's a real concern. You are being left to the mercy of medicine, technology, nurses, and doctors who will teeter from dinosaur conservatives to radical liberals. You may find yourself banging your head in disbelief at policy and procedure, administrative red tape, and the kind of bureaucracy that makes frozen molasses seem like it moves at the speed of light. But frustration merely nags helplessness on.

CONFUSION AND CONFLICTING EMOTIONS

Questions you may ask yourself daily:

- Are they saving or killing my baby?
- Is it okay for an infant so sick to be put at the end of the priority list because there are other infants clearly more "salvageable"?
- Do the doctors and nurses respect my insistency, or do they see me as a mad dog with a bone?
- When is the pain too much pain?
- Do the babies not remember the pain as some doctors suggests? So that makes it okay? Is that merely a cop-out to let us off the hook?
- Am I going mad?

preemieworld

Most likely, you'll find two opposing views on the subject of pain. One doctor on rotation will believe that, while Preemies might feel some level of pain with their underdeveloped neurons, they won't remember it. Another will err on the side of medicating if there is any question of pain; arguing that it is also easier to take care of the patient this way. Somewhere in the middle of these two perspectives lives the optimum care of the patient.

Mishaps abound in a unit like this. It is no one's fault, just the fact that science and medicine are an imperfect art form no matter how controlled by numbers. Blood gets lost. Infants **code**. Infections happen.

Living in the NICU feels like living in a mass of discrepancies and oppositions. There is no book on your baby, so without trial and error it's impossible to know how he or she will respond to medications. Then when she has a bizarre response or he encounters a side-effect, they'll tell you that it's impossible to have that kind of response. Such contradictory and concrete statements are tossed around daily, compounded by the statements of care: your baby will never get off the **vent** (your baby gets off the vent). Your baby will never walk (she is now on the track team). Your baby will never talk (you can't get him to stop his endless chatter!).

NICOLE'S TAKE:

Sometimes when I was feeling completely hopeless, the only thing that would make it better was touching Nicholas. Even if your infant is not well enough to **kangaroo**, you can do what I refer to as "reverse kangaroo" (if the mountain won't come to Mohammed…). I'd lightly lay my hand upon his torso, easily covering his entire bottom, back, and neck. My hand scale spread the length of his body. The delicate energy that passes back and forth between us is an elixir of love and a maternal suffusion through baby skin to mommy and back again. It was my way of staying connected to him, even if for only twenty minutes.

Two hands
Photo Credit: Brian Hoven

How are you, as a parent relying on these professionals who know their business, supposed to understand the unending contradictions? How can they not bother you? There are no real answers here, except to be armed with the understanding that being in the NICU is a contradiction. You shouldn't be here. Your baby should still be in your womb. If you can prepare yourself for contradiction to be a way of life, you're ahead of the game.

Point to Ponder:

Denial and Faith are strange bedfellows. They are both predicated upon the absolute belief that something is so…even when everyone and everything tells you otherwise. Who is the wiser?

DEATH, GRIEF, AND THE LOSS OF PREGNANCY

The reality is that not all Preemies have a Discharge Day. For a variety of reasons, these amazing children are too sick to continue their struggle. In any culture, death is hard to handle, yet in NICUs worldwide it just seems so very wrong.

For the family this is a tragedy that will live with them forever. They deserve great respect and dignity as they grapple with making the decisions that no parent should ever have to make for their newborn. If you are a family faced with this situation you deserve all that **family-centered care** has to offer in this situation. You have rights and you have resources.

If you are reading this section in preparation of the death of your baby, know that you have our virtual arms around you and we are crying with you. In time, you may want to talk to someone and share your grief. We highly recommend SHARE (www.nationalshare.org).

NICOLE'S TAKE:

I'll never forget the day we successfully first fed Nicholas a bottle. We finally got him to eat, and even when it was accompanied by an hour of his constantly regurgitating his formula I finally felt as if I'd done something maternal.

When I come back from a celebratory latte, I give one of the doc-

tors a big smile. He's walking toward me with a very small swaddled bundle of baby in his hands. A pink hat signifies a girl. As I approach, seeing how adorably cute she is, I suddenly realize this baby is way too small to be off a **vent**. No other leads or wires or tubes stream from her blanket.

They are heading to the in-family room. This sweet little girl, this innocent is on her way to meet her maker.

I head to the family meeting room right next door. I'm supposed to call Gwen but I cannot. I cannot pick up the phone and talk about whatever maintenance discussion we are having. I sit. And sit. I don't want to move. How do these people do this every day? How can they handle it?

When I return to see Nicholas lying peacefully in his new crib—the crib KJ has brought to him in major celebration—I lose it. I lose it in gratitude, fear, and melancholy for this baby. I only saw her once, but will never forget her exquisite face. It was the face of a **Micro-Preemie**.

When the tears fall, KJ gently lays a hand upon my shoulder. "You okay?" She asks, a bit freaked. I tell her about what I have just seen.

"I know. It's hard."

We commiserate for a while. She tells me how terrible it was for her when her little 565-grammer didn't make it after three weeks. How blown away she was. How she couldn't speak.

"How do you guys do it?"

"You just do." This answer is amazing. Because it is so simple, yet so true.

- How will my baby be sedated in order to not feel pain during this time and up until death?
- Will my doctor be around to help me during this process?
- I would like an idea of what to expect as my baby dies so that I am prepared.
- What resources and rights are available to me and my family during this process to help me through this and to also create memories of my baby.
- I would like to have a nurse who works well with families during this situation be with our family.
- I would like to call in Now I Lay Me Down to Sleep (www.NowILayMeDownToSleep.org) to help me create pictures of my baby.

NICOLE'S TAKE:

Prayer

Even if you're an atheist or an agnostic, take it from us: some form of prayer is in order—of the highest order.

You'll meet many mothers who are extremely religious or spiritual, and prayer is what gets them through their ordeal. You may not be involved in an organized religion per se, but you will find your own way of prayer to keep you spiritually and emotionally aligned.

Here's a trick that might make prayer easier for you: read your prayers to your son or daughter. They need to hear your voice.

I actually used to sing my prayers to Nicholas and before I knew it, his pent up little body would melt into this music, warbly and off-key though it might have been. The nurses took notice that when I laid my hands at Nicholas's plum sized head and cashew tender feet, and I sang my prayers to him, his oxygen saturations would immediately go up, his heart rate down.

These are not merit-less new-age exercises; even science acknowledges the advantages of the mother and father's soul connection to their baby. I never could have known the power of prayer to be so encouraging, enriching or rewarding, but I was finally able to rid myself of the utter feeling of helplessness by doing what I could for my son.

Pray.

Pray long and pray hard. Ask your higher power to help you understand these moments and give you guidance for certain situations (such as a challenging doctor or an inconsolable partner). Pray mostly, though, to let go of the feelings of helplessness.

Letting the world know about your baby's situation allows for others to come in and help in a spiritual sense. If you belong to a church/temple/synagogue, ask if your baby can be put on a prayer list. Do the same with anyone else that asks if they can do anything to help. Even if you are not a religious person, it is a truly amazing work of art when you ask others to keep your son or daughter in their thoughts every day either through prayer or through just good vibes.

If you're not spiritual, try to find some time to meditate and quiet yourself inside the chaos of all your feelings. Calmness is an antidote to helplessness and goes a long way in

helping you find a way through the black night of it all. And sometimes being proactive is your only line of defense.

There are other levels of death we have to cope with as well. It's a strange world where death is not an uncommon thing. They say in the NICU that death "comes in waves." And, as it happens, that's uncannily accurate.

PLANNING A FUNERAL

For those parents that are likely to be planning a funeral for their baby, know that we are wrapping our virtual arms around you.

This is not fair at all. But we are here to help you walk through this.

Planning. After a traumatic stay in the NICU and saying goodbye, parents are naturally exhausted and in shock. Planning a funeral is hard for anyone but especially for a grieving parent that has gone through so much.

We highly recommend reviewing the notes on this website to help start the process: ***https://childrensburial.org/first48hours/***

Expenses. These organizations currently provide grants for preemie/NICU baby/infant funerals:

- Skyler's Gift (***www.SkylersGift.org***)
- The TEARS Foundation (***www.thetearsfoundation.org***)
- The Colette Louise Tisdahl Foundation (***www.colettelouise.com***)

Grief Counseling. The death of a child is overwhelming and after the funeral life does not just "return to normal" much as well-meaning family and friends want to provide words of help.

Grieving is life-long. A grief counselor can be a huge help now and ongoing. Start with Share (***www.NationalShare.org***) for initial support.

Preemie Angel Wall. PreemieWorld has a Preemie Angel Wall where families write their angels a note.

To submit, go to ***www.PreemieWorld.com/preemie-angels***.

VIII.

LIFE OUTSIDE THE NICU —OH, IS THERE ONE?

WHAT TO EXPECT AS YOU LIVE IN A VACUUM

Is there life during and after the NICU?

Surprisingly, yes. But for any parent that is living in the hospital, the only life they know is the NICU. It's hard to find a balance when your entire universe is made up of blood draws, ins and outs, life and death situations, a new medical tribe that's become your family, and the world that you left behind. But that outside world is still chugging along with or without you doing the normal, every-day stuff.

How do you make all of this seamlessly blend together? We're not really sure that you can. From where you are, you can only have the perspective of your baby's health and well being. And if your partner is not living at the hospital, they can only have their perspective of life at home.

Try to be gentle with one another. Try to step inside the other person's shoes. If you're separating the hospital and family chores, maybe mix it up a time or two. Remember how much you love one another and that the most important thing is getting your sweet little angel home so that you can both be parents together, uniting that strength to make your family the best it can be.

And give yourself a break. Nicole barely knew we invaded Iraq, so consumed was she with the NICU. Unless one of the medical staff yells out that something is going on (which usually had to do with sports scores) you really have no clue what's going on while you're inside the hospital.

NICOLE'S TAKE:

How many nights have I woken, mid-nightmare, somehow thinking that Gabrielle is Nicholas and she's supposed to have her **ET tube**? They become interchangeable in my nebulous consciousness. I love each of them so incredibly and hate that Nicholas suffers on a daily basis; sometimes an hourly basis. Am I doing the right thing? I cannot think of many journeys that come with so much self-doubt, so many recriminations.

We all read of people nursing their sick loved ones until they pass, but what about trying to bring them to life? I felt torn in two. I needed him to be home so that life could get back to normal. And in trying to do so I allowed myself to be swept up in pushing Nicholas into a crib only to find my son was nowhere near ready. I hated myself for trying to push him too hard, loathing his environment.

And what about all the time I was spending away from Gabrielle? I discover from our nanny, Gloria, that Gabrielle has been acting out; that Gwen doesn't seem to know how to discipline her. Gloria baby-sits for us on the one night that Gwen and I were to meet at a mutual friend's birthday party. But I decide at the last minute that the party is the last place I want to be. It's 9:10 p.m.; I was supposed to meet her two hours ago, but Nicholas got a huge bump coming out of an **IV** site that we're afraid might be a bone fracture.

"I only want you to go to the party because it would be a good idea to get out…you know, be in the world," Gwen suggests.

Sure, I want a break from the hospital, but only a REAL break; not to go do something that's just going to be another demand. "If I'm going to spend time away from the hospital and it's not with Gabrielle I would like it to be with you watching an old black and white on TV."

But nothing in me finds it remotely interesting to prattle with people at a cocktail party—and talk about what? My nightmares? My OCD over Nicholas? That I have just found out my son has come down with a severe **pneumonia** and that it can be fatal? Like I want to sit around and try to explain Nicholas's condition in lay terms? I don't think so.

DEB'S TAKE:

There are times when I discuss current events with someone now and they talk about something that happened back around the time that Becky was in the NICU. I honestly think it's a dream because I don't remember that topic at all. It's as if my life had been sucked into a black hole of work, pumping breast milk, visiting Becky, visiting Becky some more, going home, and passing out.

BEWARE OF A CHANGING ADDRESS BOOK

It's times like these that you really want your family to be there for you. But sometimes you don't want them to be there with their judgments. Family is supreme and they usually do show up for you in the ways that you need. Yet because they are not exactly in your shoes, sometimes things can get a little complicated for all involved.

Conversely, you will find people that perhaps were merely acquaintances in your life suddenly showing up with food, offering to hang out with you every few weeks. You will find people whom you've just met on the ward that help you through major crises because they can relate to what you're going through.

Having to explore the depths and meaning of relationships you've held dear for years is another difficult adjustment. But there are also the amazing adjustments of seeing the strength in people that you never noticed before.

This is one of the reasons why we maintain this is such a life altering experience. It's not just the entire medical saga you're living inside, it's all the other things that change forever as well.

THE MIXED UP TRIANGLE OF IMMEDIATE FAMILY

Yet another bizarre dynamic for you to handle is that of your immediate family. Not to accuse anyone of being stuck in the 50's, but there are still quite a few husbands who go to work and are great daddies but only see their kids in the evening. If you end up with your infant in the **NICU**, you can find this wonderful and often idyllic dynamic shattered, especially if Mom ends up living in the hospital and Daddy ends up becoming Mommy and the kids get used to Dad taking them to school and taking care of the laundry and the boo-boo's. And when you do get to take a quiet Sunday afternoon at home, you feel as if you've walked into someone else's home and wonder who these people are under the body-snatchers.

If you are a husband that is used to working and coming home to a nice dinner and kids getting ready for bed, it can be just as draining and challenging for you to suddenly find that you actually have to make dinner, attend to homework, give baths, and more. And no, you don't get to watch the basketball game because your daughter needs you to lay in bed with her until she gets to sleep so the witches under the bed don't get her. Additionally, you have to wake up an hour earlier to get the kids ready for daycare and school and you have not had nearly enough sleep to go back to a demanding job. Hey, what gives? You're suddenly doing everything while your partner just gets to sit around all day at the hospital.

But that's not what it's like in a hospital. The hours drone by more boring than any job in the universe. And when they're not droning by and you're having medical crises, you only wish it was boring again.

SIBLINGS AND EXTENDED FAMILY

You may have several family members that really help you out and friends that surprise you in their steadfast support. You may also have the opposite happen.

NICOLE'S TAKE:

My younger sister (an RN) absolutely loathed her NICU rotation. She said she could never do it—never in a million years could she do this kind of medicine. She also told me that I really needed to make sure I was keeping Nicholas on this planet for Nicholas, not because I was a selfish mother who wanted her baby. She said I really had to examine what I was doing to the whole family. I wanted to slap her.

But who else was going to tell me these harsh truths? The truth was, of course, that I wanted Nicholas here because I wanted him to be here for himself. But the other truth was, yes, I am a selfish mother who wants my baby to live. Yes, I can hear the words about how this will affect the family and all that good stuff, but it doesn't really sink in. And I really can't take it in, because of course I have no earthly concept how this will affect us in the next five or ten years.

Try not to let others' thoughts and judgments affect you too strongly. While many of the things you hear from your family and friends are well meaning—and after all you wouldn't want them to tell you anything other than the truth—the reality is YOU and your spouse are the only ones who are going to live this experience. You should simply make a deal with yourself to allow your own inner voice to be the final arbiter.

YOUR OTHER CHILDREN

Most commonly a Preemie is not the only child in a family. Depending on age and maturity it is

very helpful to have siblings visit their Preemie brother/sister. And remember, simply because they are young doesn't mean you cannot bring them.

NICOLE'S TAKE:

I would bring Nicholas's sister, Gabrielle, who was only two at the time, to visit him. Having no preconceived notions of medicine or that things could be gross or "icky" she just kept saying "cool" and "wow"—her two favorite words at the time.

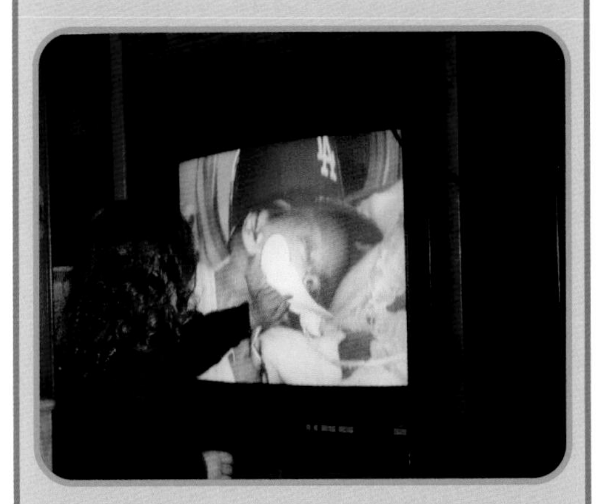

Gabrielle sees her brother on TV
Photo Credit: Brian Hoven

It also helps siblings to bond with their new brother or sister and to understand that his or her life is different. No matter how young they are, they'll "get" that this new NICU world offers unique challenges that their friends with siblings will not necessarily share. It can be a good way to ease in a sibling to another child in the family that will have medical and/or special challenges.

Bringing your other children to the hospital will also help to keep you all unified as a family and give everyone more time—the other kids, your spouse—to adjust to this new addition.

NICOLE'S TAKE:

Some have expressed disapproval that I bring Gabrielle to the NICU, but I do not want her to find this strange or terrifying (even if we all do). For her, this is simply a different kind of playground. She walks through the halls with absolute delight and fascination that her brother has come from such a unique and interesting universe. She has nicknamed Nicholas "funny bunny" on her own and now all the other babies in the ward are "funny bunnies."

I further believe that Gabrielle's early attachment to Nicholas has been what has made her bond to him so enduring. She adores Nicho-

las with an unequaled passion and she makes me so very proud in the way she cares for and acknowledges her brother. The other night we were watching "So You Think You Can Dance" and one of the dancers had a solo who was "dancing for his life." She turned to me and said, "Mommy CoCo, that's like Nicholas—his whole life is a solo." She truly understands who her brother is on the planet and how he has fought so dearly to be here.

Gabrielle joins me in a double whammy kiss
Photo Credit: Gwen Baba

GRANDPARENTS

Grandparents are hit with all sorts of emotions during the NICU stay because they are not only working through the baby being born

NICOLE'S TAKE:

Suddenly you yearn for the simplicity of tooth fairy visits, snuggle-buggles during nightmares, and arguments over Dora the Explorer versus Sponge Bob. After brushing salty foreheads with my lips every night, 365 nights a year, and suddenly not being able to hold my daughter close, smell her sweet girl-innocence, I truly realize how much I have taken for granted. When you read this you will know what I mean. Try to leave the hospital early tonight, go home, and simply be with your other precious children.

Gabrielle and Nicholas having *Monkey Jam* fun!
Photo Credit: Nicole Conn

**GIVING A GRANDPARENT
A ROLE IN THE NICU STAY**

Give the grandparents a chance to do something to help that will directly affect you and/or the baby:

- Visit the baby (but only when well!)
- Help keep information from the hospital and NICU staff organized in a folder for you and offer to keep a log of information for future reference.
- Bring mom and dad bottles of water to keep hydrated during breaks and especially so Mom is prepared to pump breast milk.
- Bring small nutritious snacks that can be eaten on the fly during NICU stay breaks.
- Offer to write up an update to family and friends on a regular basis that can be e-mailed when ready.
- Ask them to be the official photographer of the first family photo. Then do the same for them and then ask a nurse to take a photo of the entire group.
- Ask them to buy a stuffed animal that can be put into the incubator (Note: your nurse will request it fit inside a Ziploc bag so make sure it is the size of a beanie baby or smaller).
- Ask them to buy a baby blanket that can be used to cover the incubator and give the baby a womb-like darkness.
- Ask them to gently read to the baby.
- Ask them to gently sing to the baby.

early and the worries that go with it but also to have to watch their child suffer the pain and emotional trauma of it all. Just like a parent they want all sorts of information and reassurances but most of that has to come through the parent directly. They also desperately want to visit their grandchild and connect. If they allow a limited number of people to visit in your NICU, let it be the grandparents. Perhaps there are some strained emotions between you at this time but know that having them visit your child and their grandchild will do you all a world of good.

FRIENDS

One of the hardest lessons to learn when you're at the NICU is that oft spoken adage: "It's during the tough times that you find out who your real friends are." Being in the NICU makes it a little different. It's not finding out who your real friends are but rather, finding out what your real friends are made of.

Try also to not be shocked when you get attitude from friends.

Besides the losses of your regular life, it's really hard to know that dear friends and family can disappear because they don't agree with what you are doing. Or they simply find it too difficult to be at the hospital with you.

You expect your best pals to be there, and most of them will show up at least once. However, it's amazing to discover that often the people you most expect to be there with you simply cannot be. Something about the NICU opens up a whole Pandora's box of feelings, judgments, resentments that you can never know to expect. Alternatively, you will find people that come out of the wood work, people that you hardly know, being there for you in the most amazing ways.

NICOLE'S TAKE:

One of my dearest friends, with whom I had spent ten years on the phone with nearly every single day, felt I had very much made the wrong decision. Even though she didn't say so in so many words, her judgment could be felt by her absence in my life from the point that Nicholas was born onwards. To this day, our communication consists entirely of one or two e-mails a year.

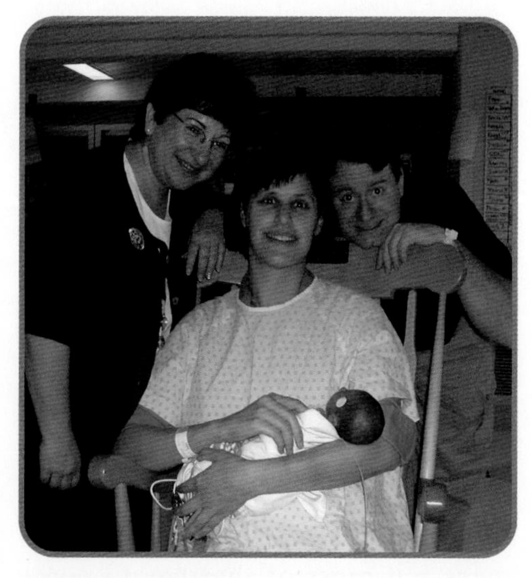

Deb, Gregg, Becky with Rabbi Amy R. Perlin, D.D.
Photo Credit: Gregg Discenza

NICOLE'S TAKE:

Two of Nicholas's three blood donors (who all donated blood often as he had **transfusion** after transfusion as well as multiple surgeries) were people I didn't even know that well. Yet there they were, like soldiers in a war: suited up, showing up time and again to gift us their precious blood. It told me a lot about who they are. The best of who people can be.

DEB'S TAKE:

You will find that many people skirt around "the question." If you haven't already had "the question" be well aware that it will occur. It is the one where your family member or friend asks what happened that caused you to have a premature baby. Insert embarrassment and guilt here. And don't forget sheer anger at the insult. This is not easy and you will have to decide how you want to answer, if at all.

NICOLE'S TAKE:

Conversely it will be difficult for you to hold your mouth when you have just gone through a life or death event, watched your child return from surgery, or make it through renal failure, and a friend complains that their baby had a 100 degree fever because they were teething. Everything is relative. People can only walk in the shoes they were handed at the door…remember that as you want to snap at a mother kvetching about a minor illness when you've dealt with God only knows what!

DEB'S TAKE:

There are people who will tell you that even though you gave birth to your child prematurely that your childbirth was nothing compared to the pain of the birth of their 9 pound baby. You went through a tough labor and delivery whether vaginally or by C-section. You likely endured a ton of medications to stop the labor as well as bed rest (some for up to weeks

and months). And now you have your baby in the NICU, a place that most people cannot even fathom because all they know is 48-hours in postpartum and out the door to home. They don't know your stress and they do not know the worries you have about the future of your child's life that is hanging in the balance. This is not a competition and the topic should not even enter the conversation, but it does.

NICOLE'S TAKE:

"Is it insane to do a birth announcement?" I ask Jen who meets us at the hospital the day after Nicholas is born.

"No, of course you should do one," she says and then offers, "Why don't you make up the text and I'll take care of getting a mass e-mail out."

And that's how Jennifer became our Team Captain.

BUILDING YOUR SUPPORT SYSTEM FINDING A HOME CAPTAIN

It is okay to lean on someone else for the little details of life. It allows you to focus on the more important issues of your life—your baby.

BIRTH ANNOUNCEMENT

So it will look a little different than the ordinary ones. It's a celebration of your baby's life coming into the world and they deserve a birth announcement like anyone else.

Without Jennifer, Nicole wouldn't have survived. She literally became Nicole's conduit to the outside world and a link between Nicole and her spouse. Being in the hospital is so time-consuming and a complete brain-drain. It doesn't help that you have to be in certain areas to use a phone and are unable to access a computer for e-mails, etc. And if there IS a computer in the family room, it's very rare that it will be unoccupied for the five minutes you want to verify that Britney Spears really did shave her head (a bizarre rumor you believe the nurses are making up).

Practically speaking, it's impossible to keep up with daily life when being forced to live at the NICU. The assignation of a Team or Family Captain can make all the difference.

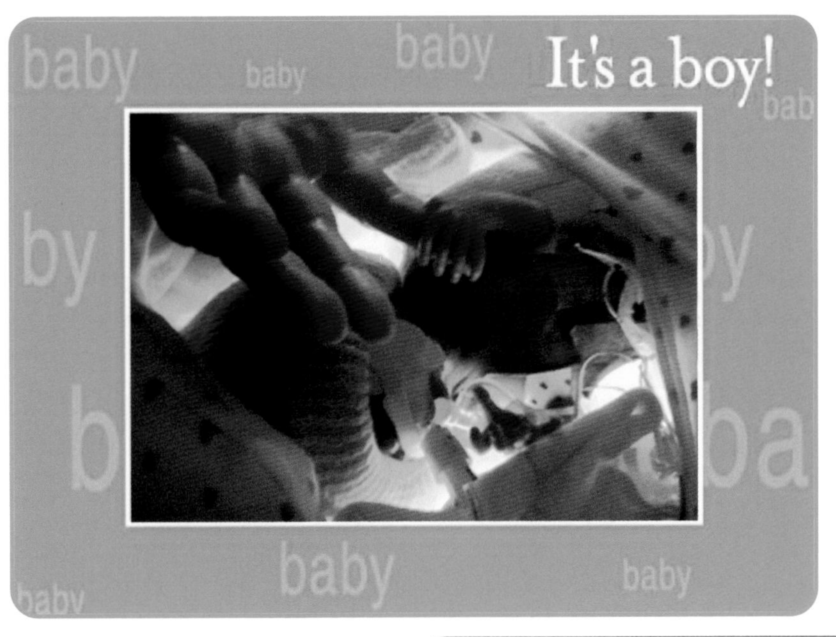

Jennifer not only ended up finalizing Nicholas's birth announcement, she sent it out and then she collated both Gwen's and Nicole's e-mail lists and sent weekly updates and emergency e-mails as were needed. When Nicholas needed yet more of his very specific blood type, she found him three donors. She grabbed Nicole that fourteenth cup of coffee when she needed it most. She bought Gabrielle's birthday presents for Nicole that year. And the one day Nicole broke out with Zoster (the only day she was not with Nicholas through the 158 days), she stood in for her, **rounded with the doctors**, and had fun making a pain in the butt of herself so the nurses couldn't get away with anything while Nicole was gone.

Name: Nicholas James Baba-Conn
Date: March 15, 2002
Time: 5:07 pm
Weight: One Pound (475 grams)
Length: Ten inches

DEB'S TAKE:

Robyn, a good friend of ours who was building her professional photography skills at the time, was one of the first people to take a picture of Becky. One of those first

photos ended up being used in our e-mail birth announcement. The text of the announcement was very simple with name, date of birth, and the usual statistics. In my husband's and my usual humor we added the text at the bottom: "She was impatient." It was how we wrapped our heads around this scary situation and made it "our normal." And in her own subtle way, Robyn helped us to achieve that new normal by aiding us with the birth announcement.

DIVIDING CHORES

It's always good when you can figure out a system wherein you feel like you and your spouse are both attending to all the myriad things that need to be taken care of, and that neither one of you is having to carry extra when you don't even feel like you can carry at all.

NICOLE'S TAKE:

My partner Gwen and I developed a system that worked for us at first. In retrospect, while it "worked" for us I don't think it was good for our partnership. I did the whole hospital thing and she dealt with the house and the bill paying.

But because we became stuck in these two separate universes, I have a feeling we did both of us and our family a disservice. I also wonder if a spouse loses out on very important bonding time with their infant when they become the "house spouse."

But sometimes you have to do what seems expedient, reasonable and in concordance with people's strengths. For the most part I think that's what Gwen and I settled on, working to our strengths, faking it where we didn't happen to have strength, and working through the stress of separation.

NICOLE'S TAKE:

Nicholas's heart condition is getting worse and his pulmonary hypertension is off the charts. I try to call Gwen and tell her I'm going to be late again. I can tell by the sound of her voice that she's not very happy. I tell her that Nicho-

las is really having a bad night, but she's heard it all before.

Gwen's biggest concern about my coming home late is that she wants to know if she needs to put Gabrielle to bed. This isn't a question of committee proportions; can't she just figure this out on her own? I mean really, next to what I'm dealing with, can't she make an executive decision? I try to give Gwen the benefit of the doubt. So I head home, crying the whole way, feeling absolutely impotent. I already know when I get home that Gwen's going to be cool and detached because I've been spending so much time at the damn hospital.

As I drive home I feel it rise, simmer, bubble over. I'm a wreck. When I call Gwen I totally lose it.

"Do you understand what he just went through?" I scream into the phone.

"Try to calm down Nicole." But I can't.

"What have I done? What am I doing to him? You should have seen him…" I stop. I'm sobbing now. I can't talk.

By the time I get home Gwen is trying to be there for me but between my being a total emotional wreck and her being detached it just isn't working.

"I'm so gone on him, Gwen," I moan as I continue to cry, separated by her from our kitchen counter.

"I love him too, Nicole." And then she breaks, "I'm…I'm so… scared."

"So am I."

"I just want him to get well and come home," she says.

"So do I Gwen, but there is a space of time between here and there."

I lose it. Gwen finally cracks. We fall into one another's arms and sob inconsolably together, both in our separate worlds of pain, but for once sharing them. It's been so long since we've touched—touched on any level. I hold on to her. Hold on for dear life.

Later we cuddle and watch TV where they are doing a feature on some sort of party.

"Gee look," Gwen mentions, "I want to be there. There—where they're having fun,"

I glance at her.

"I want to be people having fun," Gwen starts to giggle. I do too. Soon we are laughing so hard we both can't stop. Somehow people having fun seems hysterically funny to us and we both completely lose it. It is the closest we have been in months.

So what do you do when the rest of life goes on outside of the NICU? The lawn still needs to be mowed, the mail pulled from the mailbox, bills paid, family members fed, laundry done, and much more.

This is where your "Let me know if I can do anything," folks come into play. They can do something and all you have to do is get in touch with your Team Captain, the organizer for your various chores and errands. Thankfully, we live in the world of the digital age. The Internet now supplies us with the technology to reach out and ask for help without having to make a million phone calls.

Here are some go-to websites to coordinate help:

- Lotsa Helping Hands (***www.lotsahelpinghands.com***)
- Caring Bridge (***www.CaringBridge.org***)
- Care Calendar (***www.CareCalendar.org***)
- Give in Kind (***www.GiveInKind.org***)

ASK FOR HELP IN THESE AREAS:

- Meal preparation
- Childcare for siblings
- Laundry
- Housecleaning
- Grocery shopping
- Yard work
- Assistance with e-mail updates to family and friends/Blog set-up and updates
- Being at the house/apartment for deliveries
- Maintaining your calendar of appointments and reminders
- Errands around town (dry cleaning, post office)
- Creating a list of people to write thank you notes, creating mailing labels and buying stationary you can use to write these notes during quiet times in the NICU
- Buying a special box for holding special items from your baby's hospital stay, such as the first outfit worn or first hat

PREEMIE SUPPORT GROUPS: LOCAL AND ONLINE

Preemie support groups exist both locally and online, the trick is finding them. Some are NICU-based support groups from within your own hospital, while others are community-based, run by parents and/or professionals in the community itself.

To find a group in your area, check out PreemieWorld at ***www.PreemieWorld.com***.

Deb has run the following online group since 2004 and boasts tens of thousands of members worldwide: Inspire Preemie Support (***https://preemie.inspire.com***).

Two other resources are:
The NICU Parent Network (***www.NICUParentNetwork.org***) and the European Foundation (***www.EFCNI.org***)

Support groups are a lifeline for many families and are headed by parents who have been where you are now. They can be a fantastic resource for in-the-moment concerns and questions during the NICU stay and a vital resource after Discharge Day.

The lucky parents who bring their babies home often have a turning point where they want to give back and help others in the community. If you find yourself in this thought pattern at one point, volunteer! A little or a lot it doesn't matter. You can make the difference in another family's life in the way that someone else was there for you.

Preemie Directory

Whether you are looking for a support group or general preemie-related resources, chances are that our global Preemie Directory has it.

To see a full listing, simply click on the "arrowed" icon on the left, then click "All Items."

Is your organization listed here? Need to make changes? Please click here to fill out our form.

Live Search Items

Advocacy

Advocacy Orgs

Benefits

Bereavement

preemieworld

IX.

THE IMPORTANCE OF SELF CARE

When you do happen to take a few moments for yourself you are not allowed to feel guilty about it!

Taking care of yourself in the NICU is of prime importance. It's easy to have an entire day pass by without eating or sleeping—but you must keep up your strength to keep your baby going as well. Eat right, get enough rest, and drink as much water as you can down.

This concept of taking care of YOU is so very difficult when you simply want to take care of your baby. No matter how many times you hear the doctors and nurses tell you to go home and get some rest, you just know it will be better for your infant if you are there, if they can feel your presence.

Yes, it's important for your baby to know you are there and present and available. However, if you allow yourself to get sick, you won't be allowed into the NICU. Visit your own health care provider if you are having a truly difficult time sleeping or controlling your hormones. Fit in a massage if your neck is killing you from stress. Try in every way you can think of to be good to yourself. Every Mama Bear fiber in you may be screaming, "I have to take care of my baby," but the reality is that you will be no good to your baby or yourself if you get sick.

NICOLE'S TAKE:

The lovely Dr. Lily Chow once remarked to me that I was "holding up so well under the stress."

I felt like a 100-year old hag with two inches of gray that my daughter reminded me "it was time to paint." I felt like I did nothing but bitch, whine, cry, and feel constantly terrified and very often sorry for myself.

But Dr. Chow reminded me that I was there, that I showered daily, that I could make conversation. In her book, that was "holding up well" given the circumstances.

You need to be so very easy on yourself. Become the best partner

anyone could have ever dreamed up on a vision board and be that partner to yourself. Yes, hopefully your husband, spouse, partner, mother, or best friend is also playing this role. But you cannot get enough love and nurturing during this time—so you will have to fill in some of the gaps yourself. Pamper, indulge, and forgive.

WHEN IT'S TIME TO GET HELP

It is extremely common for Preemie moms and dads to experience stress to the point of needing help, especially when they have been stunned by an early birth and lost all of the "normals" that go with a nine-month pregnancy. There is no shame in the stress, but in order to be the best parents you can be, you need to get help. Your baby is counting on you to be an advocate and you need to know you have someone to turn to for assistance as well. You deserve it.

Research is coming out that fathers are also at risk for the following types of disorders along with mothers:

Postpartum Depression (PPD):

Many new mothers get this type of depression (also known as the "baby blues") after delivery or the first few months thereafter. Rather than the joys of having a newborn, the mother is depressed, crying, and often distant from her infant. So add that to a new Preemie mom and all of the medical barriers and it is a no-brainer that this has become so common in the NICU.

Check out Postpartum International (www.postpartum.net) for more support. Started by a former PPD mother, this is the ultimate resource with online chats, networks, and a mass of information.

Post Traumatic Stress Disorder (PTSD):

PTSD happens to anyone who has experienced a traumatic situation, either short or long-term. Triggers can happen day or night, asleep or awake. Like PPD, it's important to speak to a professional and gain support from family and friends. You are not being a drama queen or king; you have had the shock of your life.

NICU PSYCHOSIS

You'll be hard-pressed to find a mother or father who lives in the NICU for any period of time and doesn't go a little crazy. It's simply impossible to be in this kind of place and not be affected. Think of all the elements driving toward the perfect storm: hormones, grief, guilt, sleep deprivation, and the feeling of a loss of identity. Plus, there are so many other family dramas playing out before your very eyes—like fifteen simultaneous soap operas. You like the doctor you just saw, but now he's on rotation and you can't stand his replacement. You're getting more paperwork right and left and your brain can't even digest the paperwork you already have. You're told that your baby is doing wonderfully and two hours later hear that he was rushed to emergency surgery. To top it all off, you can never get a decent cup of coffee. How is it not possible to go a little crazy?

NICOLE'S TAKE:

Of course, there's going a little crazy and then (to paraphrase Robert Downey, Jr. in *Tropic Thunder*) there's going full crazy. Take Sara, a fellow NICU mother, who had endured nearly four months with her terminally-ill daughter. Sara relied on her Bible, was very friendly and outgoing, even in the face of her dire circumstances. She was a force to be reckoned with. Sara had always been standoff-ish when her daughter was not doing well, but things soon became more serious when her baby took a new turn for the worse.

"We can't get her CO2 down," Tony, the **RT** sighs. "We've been trying everything."

The doctor arrives, orders the lid off the **isolette**, and listens to the baby girl with his stethoscope. Several ideas are discussed as Sara rounds the corner and sees everyone standing by her daughter's bedside.

"We need to put in a larger tube." The doctor on rotation tells the team and then addresses the RT. "Let's get the next size up."

"Wait a minute." Sara jumps in. "What did you say you were doing?"

"We need to give your daughter a larger breathing tube. She's got a leak."

"But the other day you all were tellin' me how a leak was a good thing for her to have."

"But not this kind of leak. This leak is letting too much air through it. And your daughter is not being able to oxygenate."

"But don't you all need my consent to extubate my daughter?"

"We're not extubating her exactly," the doctor assures Sara. "But we do need to put a larger breathing tube in."

"But you are **extubating** her.

And I'm not going to let you do that without my consent."

"Sara, I'm trying to help your daughter."

The RT jumps in. "This is going to be fine. Your daughter really needs it."

Sara finally complies, but later that night security is called in because she's raging at the doctors. Her craziness is contagious. It's hard to leave your baby alone when you're afraid that Sara will go nuts.

As the day progresses Sara becomes more and more vocal that something is not right. Finally the surgeon flies in and agrees with Sara that her baby really needs to go into emergency surgery. To say Sara is angry is to say she's furious. She's livid with everyone who hasn't been listening to her because she's been so erratic everyone believed she was just mouthing off. I'm not sure I've ever seen anyone this angry. And it only gets worse.

That night, she was escorted out by security because she threatened the doctor that had tried to re-**intubate** the baby. The next day, she refuses to work with the nurse assigned to her daughter. Finally, after the social workers talk to her, Sara calms down and returns to her usual self. It's hard not to think of the Cheshire Cat saying, "We're all a bit mad here."

Sara's is a severe case, but it's difficult not to go temporarily insane, especially if you perceive there is any threat to your sweet, innocent baby. It's difficult to not take things personally in this unit. This is about your helpless little baby and it can be incredibly easy to turn the information you've been given around and believe that somehow *you're* not taking care of your baby. Keeping your NICU Psychosis at bay means keeping yourself in check.

Any kind of sleep deprivation makes an already frazzled person doubly-frazzled. That's a scientific fact and why we continually stress the importance of self-care. Even if you simply wander through the hospital, find a quiet place, and take a cat nap, you'll feel the results. Even 20 minutes of shut-eye can prove to be amazingly refreshing and bring a whole new outlook to a situation.

Fluids are so very important as well. You cannot drink enough water, especially in a hospital. Dehydration doesn't just make you cranky, it gives you headaches, makes you sluggish, and disoriented. And the last thing you need is for your already stressed brain to be even more maxed out.

Now when I hear plenty of liquids I'm thinking Diet Coke and coffee—but those are both diuretics so if

you're a caffeine addict like I am—or you simply become one because you're trying to figure out how to stay awake and alert in the NICU—just know that you have to drink twice as much water to make up for those kind of beverages. So you have to go to the bathroom a lot—no worries. It's good for you to get up and take a break anyway, stretch your legs and move around.

It's really hard to work out while you're in a life and death situation, but after your baby passes a critical stage, see if there is a gym in or close to the hospital. If not, try taking walks as exercise. It will do you good to get out of the hospital and breathe fresh air, and the physical activity will do wonders with your anxiety. The stimulation of walking will also help give you added energy, help you sleep at night, and clear your head.

And let's be real: there are going to be days you come in un-showered, running on two hours of sleep, feeling cranky, and in desperate need of a triple mochaccino and a chocolate-chip muffin to get your day going. So what? It's not the end of the world. You do what you have to do to get through this ordeal. And it's not a sprint in many cases. In many cases you are running the marathon of your life—so give yourself a break every so often. The one thing you must do without fail is to apply the following mantra: *I will not self-recriminate. I am doing great, I am doing the best I can. And one day we'll leave this hospital.*

> ! If you are breastfeeding and/or pumping breast milk, talk to the **Lactation Consultant** regarding what you are eating and drinking—especially caffeine. They may ask you to stop caffeinated drinks for a time but will give you some healthy and delicious alternatives.

TRUST YOUR INSTINCTS

You will soon know your baby better than anyone. And the longer you are in the NICU, the more of a specialist you will become on your own infant. You begin to notice every little nuance about your son—how he flips his hands when he's tired, how your daughter makes that funny coo when she's happy, and other things that are part of maternal instinct.

We cannot stress this concept enough. There are going to be times when you know that there is something wrong with your baby. You won't be able to point to anything concrete, but you are going to feel it in your gut. Trust that gut. It's better to be a pain in the rear at times and vocalize your concerns. Sometimes a mother's instinct is simply better than medicine.

NICOLE'S TAKE:

I believe that Nicholas is **brady**-ing so much due to his faulty **Broviac**—it's clearly clotted off. They have **TPA**'d it three times and it still isn't working. After complaining endlessly to any and every fellow, resident, doctor, and nurse, I finally go directly to the surgeon who considers my premise. Fortunately, he's willing to pull the Broviac to see if that's what's causing all the trouble.

"This is my least favorite surgery," Dr. Chen says as he begins to carve his knife into my son.

"Why is that?" I ask too soon. I become faint as he chisels away with one hand, his other fingers pressing against Nicholas's ribcage.

"There is nothing finessed about this," he explains as he grinds away at my son's chest. "It's meatball surgery."

I can't help it when I find myself hissing in anticipation. He's pulling so hard on the end of it he's either going to break Nicholas in half or the damn thing is going to snap out and the surgeon's going to land on his backside.

"If all of his bradies are connected to his Broviac, how soon do you think it would be before we see it?" I ask Dr. Chen.

"Well, it's pretty unlikely that's what's causing it. I looked at the film and it's in the right place." He's responding like all the other doctors, which is starting to peeve me because I have talked with others about the perennial disconnect between practical experience and doctoring. "But if you do see a change it would be pretty much right away."

Well, if it isn't the damndest thing. We do see a change right away. A miraculous change. Sometimes it pays for a mom to trust her instincts.

THE IMPORTANCE OF HUMOR

Finding some levity in the NICU is an absolute must. You cannot survive long in a place that is filled with so much stress, anxiety, confusion, and chaos. Much like a M*A*S*H unit, the folks who work in this medicine all have pretty keen senses of humor. The reality is that one couldn't live without it in this place. No matter how bad one of our days may be, the moms, nurses, **RT**s, and even the doctors will crack jokes whenever the opportunity arises. Give someone an opening and it will be taken.

During suctioning, the RT

farts breaking the silence in the serene bay. “Hey can we get the Hazmat people over here? Stat?”

Dr. Belagi delicately crosses his legs. “You do know the joke about cardiologists don’t you? They are the Cleopatras of medicine—the ultimate queens of denial.”

We all fell to the floor when a young child informed her mother as she watched her baby brother being breast-fed that the baby was eating her and requested, “Come on. Put her back in the cage and let’s go!”

Humor is one of the many simple pleasures that will help you to survive the NICU.

WHATEVER IT TAKES

We are firm believers in adopting the adage “Whatever It Takes” while you have to endure this journey.

Think of things that give you simple pleasure. TIVO your soaps for when you get home at night. Go to the hospital’s gift shop and load up on copies of *People*, *Us*, and any of the other magazines yammering about Lindsay Lohan’s latest stint in rehab. If you need music to survive, see if the staff will allow you to have your iPod so that you can rock out by the isolette. Do whatever it takes.

Ask your spouse if they can rub your feet. (You will have to reciprocate on these favors because remember your spouse is going through their very own hell in their new universe!). Tell your mom she just has to make you that home-made cheesecake recipe. Call your best friend and tell her she has to get you that latest book Oprah just recommended, because the hours are so interminably long that you have to have something to do while waiting for those few brief moments you get to see your baby during touch time.

Whatever It Takes!

WAYS TO TAKE A BREAK FROM THE NICU

- Go for a walk around outside the hospital so you get fresh air and vitamin D.
- Sit somewhere quiet and meditate. Hospital chapels are a good place that do not necessarily need to be for religious purposes.
- Read a book or listen to an audiobook that provides you with some sort of escape.
- Take a day off from the NICU. Seriously, this is totally okay. If you are concerned you will call in checking on the baby, ask a grandparent to “baby sit” for you at the unit. They will jump at this and the nurses will keep the grandparents in check. Consider it perfect training for when discharge day happens.

X.

RESOURCES:

YOUR NEW BEST FRIENDS

Whatever resources you find, take advantage of them. Sometimes the greatest assets come in the simplest packages (a fact you are probably well aware of by now), and occasionally you don't realize a resource that's staring you in the face.

Some hospitals, such as Cedars-Sinai, have a regular Parents' Night for moms and dads to mix and mingle. Others have holiday parties, coffee-klatches, or other informal gatherings for parents who have been there. While you may want to be bedside at first, you'll find that you can help your child—and yourself—by meeting and commiserating with others. The added care, warmth, and gentle support are also major pluses.

From our perspective one of the best all round resources is another NICU mom. In fact, Monica, one of the parent liaison moms, became Nicole's NICU angel. Monica happened to be working as a volunteer in the post-op surgical wing and it seemed like every single time Nicole was alone up in the bay and having a particularly difficult time, she'd POOF—appear. It was uncanny. Nothing beats being guided by the "been-there-done-that" advice and experience of a fellow NICU Mom. And it might be something you'd like to consider becoming yourself, once your baby is at home, healthy, and you've all adjusted back to regular life.

As you were reading through this book, you may have come across some important resources along the way. Some of these will help you through the NICU days, some will come in handy afterward, and some bridge both extremes. Mom-to-mom, these are our top picks:

- ***PreemieWorld.com:*** We have created a fabulous world that supports Preemie families and professionals. Check out our downloadable PDFs, newsletters, freebies aplenty, and our storefront filled with products to celebrate and relate to our worldwide community
- ***LotsaHelpingHands.org:*** Especially helpful for Team Captains looking to establish an efficient way to navigate all of those won-

derful and caring volunteers in your life.

- ***Preemie.Inspire.com:*** Started by Deb in 2004 with just a few people, it has grown and expanded boasting over 50,000 families worldwide. Discussions revolve around NICU, home, school, disability post-preemie pregnancy, Preemie Angel families and more.
- ***NICUParentNetwork.org:*** This organization has support group members throughout the United States and a couple of international organizations.
- ***EFCNI.org:*** This group has members across Europe but also around the world. A great way to find a support group.
- ***NationalPerinatal.org:*** This organization has a professional side and a Family Advocacy Network made up of support groups from all over. Lots of great support materials to pick from.
- ***NICDAP.org:*** The NIDCAP Federation International, NFI, promotes the Newborn Individualized Developmental Care and Assessment Program (NIDCAP) in hospitals and encourages its use nationally and internationally to support the growth and development of premature infants and to improve the quality of their care and the support for their families.
- ***ZeroToThree.org:*** This non-profit promotes public policy and healthy infant development in the parent and professional worlds. Their parent section is rich with materials on developmental delays and the like.
- ***ParentsAsTeachers.org:*** In addition to parenting tips, these folks have a program that will assist families with home visits, parent group meetings, screenings and a resource network to help families get the help they need and help their child thrive.
- ***CDC.gov/RSV:*** Hand-washing, staying home when sick, RSV… the Center for Disease Control comes in handy when it comes to setting ground rules for friends and family. Use this site for information and if needed ask the doctor for a note you can have on hand.
- ***All About Preemie Nutrition:*** An Exclusive Human Milk Diet: ***https://preemie.us/HumanMilk-PW*** and Helping My Tiny Baby Thrive: ***https://preemie.us/Action-Plan***

XI.

EEK! PREPARING FOR DISCHARGE DAY

Congrats! Freaked out? Sure! Get ready for another "new normal" and be sure to make it special for you, the baby, and your family.

"Most parents who have had a long stay want to stay as badly as they want to leave."

-Social Worker,
Cedars-Sinai Hospital

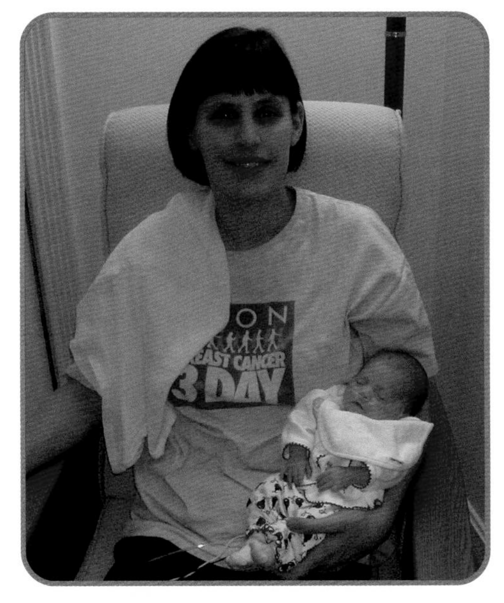

We're home!—WHEW!
Photo Credit: Gregg Discenza

ALL EMOTIONS ARE OKAY

You will truly run the gamut of emotions, not only during your preparations to leave but at the actual time of departure. It used to be you watching other babies and their families leave. While you were happy for those lucky folks, you probably also felt a sort of tugging envy that it couldn't be you leaving.

NICOLE'S TAKE:

I'll never forget when the insurance assessors told us on day 95 of our stay that they had assessed that Nicholas would be in the NICU for 230 days. I almost fainted. I was already DONE on day 95, how could I make it through over one hundred more?!

But when I discovered we would indeed be leaving earlier, I totally panicked. Part of the panic

came in because we just simply weren't ready. And part of the panic was valid—they were actually pushing Nicholas to get out of the hospital before he could be "killed by the cure." (see **Iatrogenic Activity**) To their credit, they also knew that he was going to receive 24/7 nursing and that it was time for us to care for him at home with help. So why did it feel like we were being cast-away to a desert island? I did feel truly scared that first night, when we were doing our **Rooming-In** stay—our see-if-we-can-do-this-on-our-own night—even when I knew I could ring the button to get assistance if needed. It wasn't that night that was giving me the sweats but the nights that would follow. Could we really do this? And, of course, the answer is yes.

Know that feeling as terrified as you are happy is completely normal. Sad, wistful—I actually was freaking out because I realized there was a part of me that was going to miss the hospital and the people in it. This is where I had lived for the past 158 days. I was totally confused about all the emotions I was feeling.

Try to find a mom that's just gone home. Get her number and talk to her about how she's coping.

DEB'S TAKE:

I was a complete wreck on Discharge Day. So nervous! I mentioned this quietly to our primary nurse and she said it was okay and that I knew what to do and I would be fine. After packing us up with more diapers, wipes, and blankets than we knew what to do with and giving us a special card with Becky's footprints, we were on our way. The whole way home and throughout the next day I lived with Nurse Donna's careful and caring instructions on how to handle Becky's medical equipment and medications. It was as if there was an angel whispering in my ear each step of the way. Wow, I did know what to do.

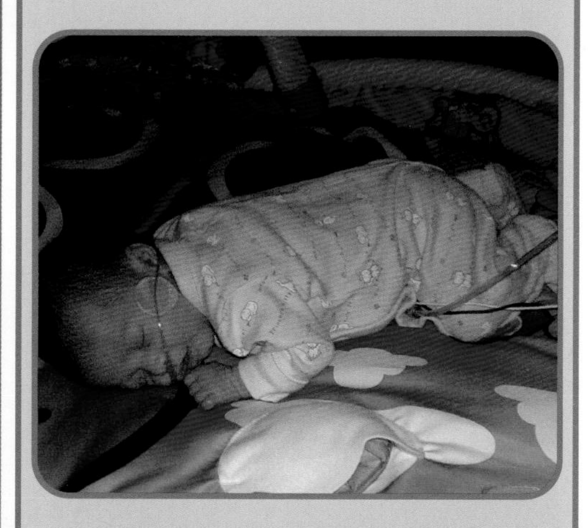

Becky does tummy time at home
Photo Credit: Deb Discenza

Leading up to Discharge Day, you will be assessed by the medical professionals in order to ensure that you are able to care for your baby at home. Even when it seems like there is no such thing as going home without being completely prepared, rest assured that they are looking out for you as well as your infant. More than likely, you will also have a Rooming-In night, particularly if you have had a long stay or if your infant has a challenging medical journey. It's critical that you are able to cope with anything that might come up in the middle of the night, and this dry-run is an excellent way to prepare for life at home.

DEB'S TAKE:

I was absolutely freaked out about taking Becky home. As she was coming home on medical equipment I fully expected we would be "**rooming in**" with her one night prior to discharge. For whatever reason, it never happened, and suddenly there Gregg and I were with our infant that was outweighed by her accessories. To top it off, we couldn't have family and friends there to welcome us home due to the fact that it was **RSV** season and we were basically on lockdown.

No matter how unsure you are about moving into this next chapter of your life, you will get through it. Have a serious and truthful discussion with your partner; tell them that you're scared about coming home, that you don't know how things are going to feel. Are you returning to your old roles? Have you found that mixing the roles up is better for you? Once your baby is home, your time and availability will be a bit squeezed as you transition, so it is important to have an idea of who will take care of what beforehand.

MAKING IT SPECIAL

Discharge Day is a wonderful time to capture some of what you have lost: a normal homecoming. What's more, as a parent that has survived the NICU, you have a chance to give back and say thank you in a way that new "everyday" parents can't.

You have formed friendships that will continue with annual visits to the NICU. You can honestly call some of the doctors and nurses family. They witnessed your pain in the most intimate moments and helped

you through some of the darkest days more than anyone outside the NICU could have. They get it.

NICOLE'S TAKE:

After all those days in the hospital I could hear the soundtrack to that old B&W TV show called "Branded" with Chuck Connors all young and square-jawed. In the opening credits, he is branded as a traitor and loses all of his possessions.

While we were in no way traitors, what it reminded me of was starting over, taking all the old stuff down and starting new. Stripping down pictures. Undoing his little mobile. Putting away his miniature stereo system. Taking down all of Nicholas's accoutrements we had put up over the months to make this Nicholas's corner of the bay. It really was Nicholas's corner—make no mistake—but now it would become someone else's.

SOME TIPS ON HOMECOMING:

- **Baby Outfit:** Pick a special outfit that was either already given to you or that you pick up yourself. Dress your baby up and take lots of pictures with doctors and nurses.
- **Party Like it's Discharge Day:** Take some time to celebrate this moment with the staff with a handwritten note, a card, or (if possible) some treats. Professionals love these celebrations and even a simple thank-you means the world to them.
- **Make a Special Exit:** As you walk your baby out the door, take pictures and walk proudly. You did it: you are on your way home! And do the same walking through the lobby. Give yourself that moment you lost at your post-childbirth discharge and create a new memory of walking out with your baby.
- **It's All Right to Cry:** Life has changed and so have you. You are in a new world, but you are strong. Let the tears flow and let go. You are bringing your baby home.

NICOLE'S TAKE:

We had a little party of sorts, celebrating this miracle day that Nicholas was going to get out of the hospital (when of course no one ever thought he would). Gwen and I had purchased special little gifts for all of Nicholas's primaries, pharmacist, **OT,** and **PT** as well as several of my favorite doctors.

It wasn't anything grand, just a token of our genuine appreciation and affection for all the care these folks had devoted to Nicholas and his well-being. We had a little cake; we did a bunch of goodbyes. We went from being a family having a party, but soon Becky was called away for an emergency. And Jovan, our favorite RT, had to take care of a vent change. People scattered back into what they had to do: life in the NICU.

We did what they call "the walk"—a sort of ceremonial rights of passage—walking down the hallway of the bay, stopping to say special goodbyes to some of the other families with whom we had connected, and having our last look.

And then we headed to home, sweet home.

PICKING A PEDIATRICIAN:

When you've been through such a rough journey with your child, having the right pediatrician makes all the difference in the world. Make sure that the doctor you ultimately pick is going to work well with all of your baby's issues. Ask the NICU doctors and other NICU survivors for a recommendation and do your research.

Also a very critical component of picking the right pediatrician is to start your search early. Many doctors round on a daily (sometimes weekly) basis on infants they are actively seeing in the NICU. The earlier you can choose a pediatrician, the better your baby's doctor will know your infant and all the medical challenges she comes home with. This way your pediatrician can speak to the **neonatologists** on the floor as well as any specialists involved with your infant's care.

NICOLE'S TAKE:

Nicholas was lucky in so many ways, but one of the principal ways in which he really hit the jackpot was with his primary care

physician post-NICU. I'll never forget the first day I saw Dr. Kimberly Diamond (La Peer Pediatrics) sitting by Nicholas's **isolette**: my first thought was, "She's too young to be a doctor." She may have the most youthful face, but man did this woman know her stuff. And whatever she didn't know, she wasn't afraid to ask the specialists. She also ended up doing a ton of coordinating with all of Nicholas's myriad doctors as well as massive amounts of paperwork for all the different state and county funding sources for which Nicholas was eligible.

I always say that Nicholas simply has the best pediatrician in the world. And I mean it. Dr. Diamond not only made several house visits in the first critical years, she always kept Nicholas's huge file (which she put into several notebooks) on her desk and would not allow anyone in her office to remove them. This ensured that she had quick and easy access to his ever-growing records. We were literally on the phone daily at times and she is an amazing communicator. She also has such a gentle sense of humor and warmth that she made even the scariest of times seem bearable.

It's critical to find a doctor with whom you can create a teamwork approach to getting your child as well as possible, especially when there are multiple medical challenges and/or chronic problems. You will be entering into an important partnership for years to come. When you are able to find a doctor like Kim Diamond, you will not only feel more reassured that things are going to get done correctly, you will feel like you have a true ally when it comes to making critical decisions. This is key in your child's ongoing care.

Make a list of questions to help you guide your decision making, but also listen to your gut. Yes, you need to find a professional that really understands the neonatal end of medicine, but you also need to find a person with whom your personalities mesh. You will need to work together, and more likely than not will go through some stressful times.

Questions for Interviewing Pediatricians

- What kind of experience do you have with babies graduating from the NICU? Who else in your practice has that kind of experience?
- Does your practice feature sepa-

rate sick and well visit waiting rooms?

- Can fragile infants be shown directly into a room upon arrival and wait there?
- What are your sick visit schedules on evenings, weekends, and holidays?
- How do you handle test requests for suspect matters?
- What is your opinion on **Early Intervention**, ChildFind, and Special Education programs for at-risk children?
- Is there a **Lactation Consultant** on staff to help with breastfeeding issues?
- What well-check schedule does your practice follow for Preemies upon discharge? Is it the same as non-Preemies?
- What is the on-call procedure and how quickly does a doctor call back?
- What insurance does your practice take? Do you also work with state and county funding?
- What are the backgrounds of the doctors in the practice? Do I get a choice of doctors for the primary doctor? What about for sick visits?
- Is there anything else you would like me to know about your practice and its philosophy?

NOTES:

____

____

____

____

____

____

____

____

____

____

____

____

____

____

____

____

____

DISCHARGE PAPERS

Make sure you get copies of everything. Everything.

Duplicate your copies because you never know when you, a specialist, a paramedic, or a visiting nurse will need this information after you handed your last copy to someone else. You don't want to hunt for this stuff—especially if you're heading to the ER—and you especially don't want to rely on

your memory for your child's allergies or the specific procedure performed on your infant in week three of the NICU, while you were still in a total fog.

When you have a medically fragile infant, the paperwork will bury you. Sometimes it feels truly insurmountable. The earlier you get this together, the better for you—and your mental health. With many of the services you'll be using post-NICU, you MUST have the proper paperwork. Moreover, it must be signed by the proper channels whether it's your primary care physician, specialist, or therapist. Like the hospital staff, if you treat paperwork with the respect it deserves you'll find that your life will run more smoothly.

This new golden rule is especially true for any kind of social services that you receive. You may be juggling multiple insurance carriers, each with their own bureaucracy. Organize a book for each provider and subdivide by specialist and/or specialized service. If you start out right, it will be much less of a problem for you later.

NOTES ON CARE

When you leave the hospital you will be assigned a discharge nurse. This nurse will be completely familiar with all the elements of discharge that are necessary for you to leave and include notes on the care that you are to provide your child.

It's possible that your infant will leave the hospital with **monitors**. Hospital staff will first in-service you, usually with the technician from the DME (Durable Medical Equipment) company who will also train you on running the equipment. Your discharge nurse will set up these meetings and services.

When these technicians come to the hospital or your home, ask if you can record them as they go through the procedures required to run any of the equipment. Chances are, you are going to be completely overwhelmed when you return home.

The other issues around home care are Home Health Nursing and coordinating with several pharmacies. In these cases, it's once again a good idea to organize this as a spreadsheet or binder as you build your own home version of the NICU.

INFANT CPR

You MUST become certified in infant **CPR** before you leave the hospital. For many, this may seem scary—everything you would be doing on an adult for CPR seems brutal and harsh to begin with and therefore feels doubly-so with a small child (especially one who may have fragile bones or weighs under five pounds). It's hard not to be terrified. However, no matter how scared you are, CPR could save your baby's life.

Tape a CPR chart to the wall in your baby's room. Practice compressions and breathing against your forearm once a week so that the rhythm becomes second-nature. Keep your infant CPR current. Your home health nurses must have their CPR current and, in most states, they must be re-certified on an annual basis in order to practice.

Check with your NICU to see if they offer **CPR** classes within the unit. If so, it could be not only cost-effective (i.e.: free), but also more focused on your infant's needs than a public class.

DEB'S TAKE:

The NICU Nurse told us to go ahead and sign up for an infant **CPR** class, which we did through the hospital's public education program. We didn't realize that the NICU had its own private class. In hopes of getting everyone acquainted, the public class teacher asked us to go around the room and introduce ourselves and say a bit about why we were in the class. Starting with me. How bad is it to tell a room full of Moms-to-be that your baby was born early and that she is in the NICU? You would have thought that prematurity was a disease that was catching the way the entire room gasped. Even though everyone let out a relieved sigh when I told them that she was doing well and was preparing to come home, I wanted to crawl under my table and hide.

WE'RE HOME! NOW WHAT?!

If you know that you are going to require Home Health Nursing, you are probably under the assumption that this will be a much easier road given that you are in your own home and will be in charge of who you hire (paid for by insurance or state/county funding sources). However, your home is about to turn into an entirely different universe. Learning from some past mistakes can also be the life-saving difference between being chained to your infant's medical challenges 24/7 and being able to have a relatively balanced life.

HOME HEALTH NURSING TIPS

- ONLY use a reputable agency. Some will send over "nurses" who have received trumped-up licenses or don't understand the basic concepts of hygiene (true story). Don't be afraid to turn these people away at the door.
- Home Health Nurses are a whole new breed. If they are dyed-in-the-wool HHNs, they will not even remotely resemble the professional and proficient nurses you just left at the hospital. Ask your potential nurse if she also works out of a hospital. HHNs who have hospital experience are generally free from any personality disorders that precludes them from working with people. Such experience will also ensure that they are up-to-code on their nursing skills. A hospital will not keep a nurse employed who is incompetent—it's simply too much of a liability.
- Prepare a list of questions (in addition to hospital experience) for each potential nurse. This will help you assess their level of competency as well as their dedication to the work. Do they have family? If they have a lot of family and many kids, know up front that when those kids become sick, the nurse is going to become a mother first and will have to call off if she needs to take care of her own children. Find out how long they've worked in the field. What was their last case? Why are they no longer there? You can also ask the agency about the nurse's last case to verify that she wasn't fired for misconduct.
- Know that you are going to have to be around this nurse 8-12 hours at a time. If she's a Chatty-Cathy and you know you won't be able to handle the incessant conversation, it's not going to be a good fit. See how the nurse also deals with your other children (if any) and partner. Is there a personality rub?
- Also know that a nurse, like anyone else, can give a great interview. You will never really know until they do a shift how they are going to work out. Don't be afraid to interview as many different nurses as you need to find the RIGHT nurses for you and your baby.

DEB'S TAKE:

Our Home Health Nurses were actually **Visiting Nurses** for the first few weeks post-NICU. They would show up and check over Becky and see if we had any questions. One nurse in particular loved to go on about her son who was a Preemie and how difficult it was to have a Preemie and more all the while shooting out requests at me to get this and get that. At her next visit she did much of the same and barked more orders and we ran around. Suddenly she stared at me and said, "Wow, Mom, you look tired. You should get some rest!" It was all I could do not to scream, "Good idea. Don't let the door hit you in the back!" It didn't help that I never knew what to ask these nurses.

Things you should remember:

- This is *your child.*
- This is *your home.*
- This person is being paid by *you.*
- If this person isn't good personality fit, call the manager and request someone else..
- If they are not useful, ask the doc to discharge them.
- If you need something specific, call their manager.

Questions For Visiting Nurses:

- What are the results of my baby's exam?
- When is the next visit?
- Am I able to schedule the visit so it does not interrupt my child's (and family's) rest time?
- Is there anything else I need to know at this time concerning my child's health?
- Can I have a report of my child's visit?

NICOLE'S TAKE:

Sept 1 2002

OYYYY: I remember when I used to work in a restaurant and staffed 31 waitresses who all had life traumas, boyfriends leaving them, ex-husbands stealing children, and always the car breaking down, but I've never heard some of the excuses I did when I became my own little ICU administrator: the house burned down, I jabbed my jaw into a rocking chair leg, I suddenly forgot my brother's in from El Salvador and he's trafficking illegal contraband, the Indian tribal council is calling a special meeting. It never lets up…I spend more hours on the phone regarding staffing than I do with all the incompetent medical supply people!

It is ten days now since Gwen and I have been home. We've gone through as many nurses. It's difficult to find nurses with bona-fide experience: One of the nurses responded when I asked her if she had experience in pediatrics; Yes. I have two kids. That was the sum total of her experience!

One nurse, Crazy Horse Winona—If you say anything ANYTHING —like for instance "Nicholas's night nurse showed me how to change his ostomy bag." She will respond in kind with "Did you ever hear the legend of the faceless corn husk?" on and on it goes until I want to be Scarlett hitting Prissy, feel the sting in my hand at the inanities I must endure because we now live in a world called Critical Patient at Home Psychosis.

The other side of this particular universe known as Home Health Nursing are the nurses that come into your life and literally become part of your family. They tell you not to get too personally involved with the nurses the agency sends you, but, when you have someone taking care of your most precious cargo 12 hours a day, it's a little difficult not to become attached. For us, we are proud to call Nicholas's nurses family—and it truly does take a village!

Zel, Nicholas' special *Nana*
Photo Credit: Nicole Conn

Auntie Dan-Dan with Nicole and kids
Photo Credit: Alissa Broderdorf

LIFE AT HOME: MEDICAL EQUIPMENT, SUPPLIES, AND PRESCRIPTIONS

Perhaps Nicole was naïve. She thought if you called and placed an order for medicine or supplies, you would actually get that order in a timely manner AND get what you ordered.

Oh no. It doesn't work that way.

There is the seemingly arbitrary decision as to whether or not you are covered for the items you have requested. There's the balance with multiple insurance carriers. And then there's the very distinct possibility that you receive the wrong order.

We're going to let you in on a little secret: Never underestimate the influence and power of someone who wants to help you.

Forge relationships with someone at each of the main supply houses and pharmacies you will be using. Send them Christmas cards, ask how their day is, thank them profusely. This will truly save your life—and your sanity.

THE MAGIC OF NOTES

Keeping notes in a single place on your phone, your tablet or your computer or even in a notebook is worth gold. Everytime you call the insurance company, log it. Same with the pediatrician, pharmacies, Early Intervention team members, surgeons, hospitals, etc. Having your world organized with keep you on top of everything while everyone else is being less than organized and potentially overcharging you.

We suggest logging the following: date and time, category (insurance, doctor, etc.), name of person, information relayed, follow-up needed.

HANDICAPPED PARKING TAGS

Yes, you think, your child is handicapped in some ways. But you're not and you're the one strolling him into the doctor's office. You don't want to take a parking spot away from someone who has to get to the doctor's office themselves and truly cannot walk. You'll get over this after your first doctor's visit, and fast.

If your child is coming home on medical equipment, you should be eligible for a 6-month temporary handicapped hang tag. Go onto your state's DMV website and download the proper form. Complete the form and bring it to your

NICU doctor prior to discharge to get it signed so you can get the tag ahead of time.

Don't feel bad about getting yourself a handicapped parking tag. Trust us: your child is indeed handicapped at this particular time in her life and you need all the help you can get, especially once you have to schlep your child, stroller, oxygen tank with cannula, and their **apnea** and **brady** monitor with all the leads half a block away from your pediatrician's office.

RE-ENTERING PUBLIC LIFE RSV SEASON

Respiratory Syncytial Virus (RSV) is a very serious complication for our infants, especially for those of you who have had vented babies with chronic lung disease. A head-cold for most folks is no big deal, but when your Preemie catches it you will see how amazingly sick they become and how long this illness lasts.

Your infant will get sick. It's the nature of the beast, and of course you want your child to have some illnesses to build up their immune system. But for our kids, this is a terrifying prospect. The last place you want to end back up at is the hospital.

LAYING DOWN HOUSE RULES

WASH YOUR HANDS. That's rule number one. This is critical. Your friends may think you are OCD about hand washing and hand sanitizer bottles on every shelf in every room of your home. But the reality is that germs are primarily transmitted from hand-to-hand contact.

Preemies are incredibly susceptible to getting sick, but you still want your friends and extended family back in your life. Clean hands help to remedy these two situations. If your baby is pre-surgical or experiencing any illnesses, you are also within your right to have guests wear masks—particularly guests who think they are sick or living with someone getting over a cold.

Which leads to the next obvious rule: DON'T HAVE GUESTS OVER IF THEY'RE SICK. You don't want to be anti-social, but once you've gone through the first few illnesses with your baby you'll relive all the terrors of the hospital (not to mention some PTSD). It's natural, and its okay for you to set limits with family and friends around the safety and well-being of your child.

Don't allow people to guilt you into feeling like you're being over the top. Let them stand in your shoes. Once they've had a child go off the **vent** only to immediately go back on due to one little germ, then they can tell you how overwrought you are being. Meanwhile, you're practicing common sense given your previous history.

RETURNING TO THE HOSPITAL

It's the smell.

For many NICU vets, the smell, the look, and the feel of the hospital will make them queasy one,

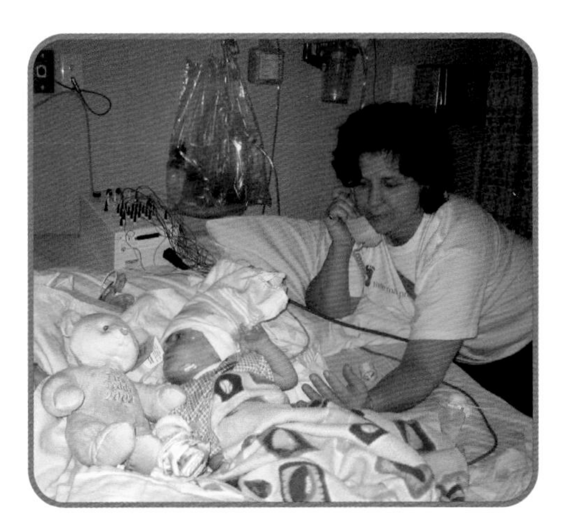

Endless life in hospital
Photo Credit: Victoria Alonso

five, even twenty years later. So many of us ended up living in these units for so long and we are all victims of PTSD. It's no wonder why it's so difficult to return.

Everyone tells you that you will and you pray that you won't.

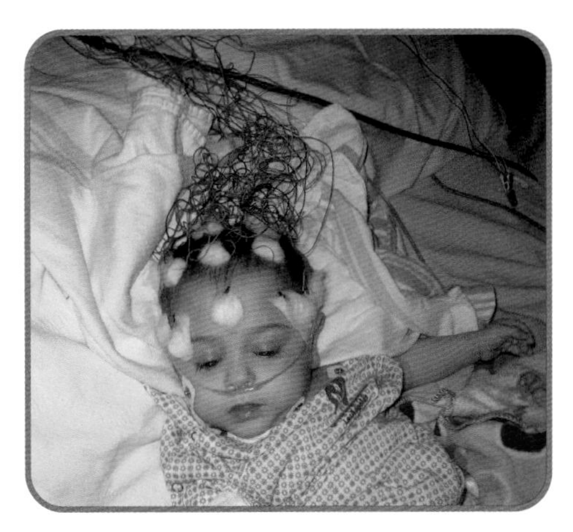

Nicholas as *Bride of Frankenstein*
Photo Credit: Victoria Alonso

Some of us have recurring and chronic issues that simply will not go away after the NICU stay. Your primaries may tease you on Discharge Day that you'll never come back to visit unless you have to. And initially, you will know in your heart of hearts that you'll be back. You consider these people your family; you bonded with them in an intense period of time. But after being home for a few months, the last place in the world you want to return to is the hospital, no matter how much you miss the people who saved your child's life over and over again.

WHAT A DIFFERENCE TIME MAKES:

Going back to the NICU after your child is discharged is an interesting experience. Your whole being is assaulted with memories whether it be the reception desk where you checked in, the hand washing station or those doors to your baby's bay. Some are good, some are not so good. But all are valid. You may want to cry and should. It's okay and it is nothing the staff hasn't seen or heard before. They know where you have been and they know that this is part of the healing process.

So you ask—why in the world would I want to go back to the NICU? For a number of reasons you will be compelled to return:

1. To celebrate your child's birthday (people go back for years, even decades—no joke).
2. To see your favorite staff members and to show off your amazing Preemie.

NICOLE'S TAKE:

I think I miss the hospital. Not the hospital of course—I miss the care of the nurses. I miss my routine. I miss my double mocha at 11:30 after rounding. And I really miss Judy, Becky, KJ., Stephanie, Lori, Agnis…I miss my sorority. I miss their care.

Let me just officially state here and now for any nurses that I had skirmishes with—even Big Bertha—you are all goddesses. You walk on water. You are extraordinary and exceptional.

The one bit of solace you can take with you is this: On the Pediatrics Floor, moms rule. While in the NICU, the nurse, doctor, and staff are all the first point of care for your child. You're hardly allowed to be a mom in the beginning. But once you head to Peds, you will learn that the staff knows moms and parents are their best friends. While returning to the hospital is a stressful situation, you will get the respect you deserve.

Items you could bring to the NICU that will make the day of every team member:

- A picture of your child while in the NICU and now.
- A thank-you card detailing how things went after discharge.
- A thank-you card that recognizes what the staff helped you with during the stay.
- A bunch of flowers with your name on the card.
- A plate full of cookies or other treats.

3. To go back to the world where your worries and concerns were validated as opposed to the outside world that just did not "get it."

When you come back to the NICU, and you will at one point, make sure to give the staff members a little thank you. Not everyone will be there the day you show up and many people on the off-shifts will be grateful for your thoughtfulness.

NICU FOLLOW-ALONG CLINIC:

Many hospitals have a Follow-Along Clinic where your child can be assessed at certain intervals over 2-3 years to track development and more. If your hospital has this program and your child qualifies for it, do not walk—*run* to get that first appointment set up after discharge. This is an important way for you to have your child evaluated to see if there are any areas of development that are delayed and need help from your local **Early Intervention** program. Getting evaluated early is a big part of giving your child that edge in catch-up. When you go in for your appointment there will be a team assembled to evaluate your child's various areas of development. Make sure to bring a list of

DEB'S TAKE:

Every year we try to go back to the NICU on Becky's birthday to see the staff and show them how "Discenza Girl" has grown. They love every minute of it because it is an affirmation of all of their hard work, day in and day out. Often the relationship between parent and staff members can often evolve into a strong family-like connection. They know where you've been and how tough the journey was for you and your child. There is no need for translation, no need for detailed explanations. Just a knowing smile and a joyful tear says it all.

Gregg & Becky at NICU Reunion
Photo Credit: Deb Discenza

concerns and questions with you.

NICU REUNIONS:

After your baby is discharged, you might receive an invitation by mail regarding the hospital's "NICU Reunion." Many NICUs have these and if you go you will be able to catch up with other moms you once knew, connect with staff members and have a great party. When you have time, contact your NICU and ask them when their next reunion will be held.

Becky mugging for the camera
Photo Credit: Robyn Kuniansky

Nicholas with *Mickey* at Cedars' Reunion
Photo Credit: Kristin Keller

CONGRATS!

Congratulations on making it to this very special moment in your baby's NICU stay. We are honored to have been a party of your journey. Know that you are a different person than when you first entered the

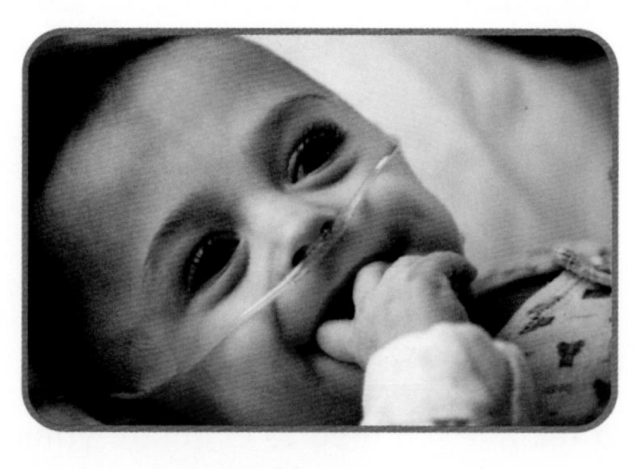

Nicholas, happy at home
Photo Credit: Brian Hoven

XII.

PREEMIE PARENT POWER

- As you leave the NICU with your baby, realize that you are a changed person.
- You live life one day at a time because you understand that life can change in an instant.
- You understand that life is truly fragile because you have watched your baby struggle day in and day out.
- You are resilient because you know that to be your baby's parent you have to bounce back from the trauma and focus on the moment and the joys within.
- You are strong in mind because you have handled a stressful situation and knew what to ask and how to help your baby.
- You are strong in body because you know that you have to take care of yourself to be the best parent you can be.
- You know the true meaning of joy because you have held your baby in your arms after wondering if that would ever be possible.
- You are an advocate for your baby and have talked with doctors and specialists with knowledge about your Preemie that no other parent can truly conceptualize.
- You are an advocate for yourself, making sure that you are clear with others in terms of what you want that is best for you and your family.
- You have the power to vocalize your requirements in terms of how your baby is handled in the real world. You stare down adversaries who refuse to wash hands at visits and believe that to be okay.
- You are capable of organizing more than you ever thought possible—daily routines, medical and therapeutic appointments, insurance matters—all while the rest of life continues at its feisty pace.
- You no longer let the small things bother you. You know what is and what is not worth worrying over.
- You understand that what you have been through has changed your life forever and that not everyone else will understand that. You have a new passion and a new reverence for all that life has to offer.
- You leap over all problems in an effortless bound—you truly are a supermom!
- You believe in gratitude and no longer take ANYTHING for granted.
- You believe in miracles. Your baby is one. And you helped make that happen.

NICOLE CONN

—Writer/Director/Editor/Mother

Nicole Conn has been a die-hard romantic and black and white film fan from the age of nine. Her penchant for adult and dramatic story telling is evident in her latest critically acclaimed feature film, ***A Perfect Ending*** – "the sexiest film of 2012" (Curve) and with over 55 million views to her sneak preview online, ***A Perfect Ending*** is now the single best-selling film of its genre.

Conn's previous venture, ***little man***, is a documentary she wrote, directed and produced about her own premature son born 100 days early and only weighing one pound. The feature documentary went on to win 12 Best Documentary Awards, Conn has achieved world-wide industry recognition with her films ***Claire of the Moon***, ***Elena Undone*** (which boasts the LONGEST KISS IN CINEMATIC HISTORY), ***A Perfect Ending***, and little man. Winner of many film awards, she was was a finalist in the prestigious Academy of Motion Picture Arts and Science's Nicholl Fellowships in Screenwriting.

She has currently finished her eighth film, ***More Beautiful for Having Been Broken***, another strong message film about special needs based on her personal experiences with her son, Nicholas, who is very special needs and remains medically fragile and her daughter, Gabrielle, who makes her film debut in what critics describe as a "heart-breakingly beautiful love story." She is also finalizing her epic tome, ***Descending Thirds***, which is in development for the big screen along with her next feature, ***Do We Not Bleed***.

***The Conn Family Today**: Gabby, Nicole, Nicholas*

Photo Credit: Marina Rice Bader

DEBORAH DISCENZA

—Author/Publisher/Mother

Combining careers in the technology and publishing fields, Ms. Discenza is continuing her journey to educate and support others through publications, the web and speeches as she takes the helm of CEO of ***www.PreemieWorld.com*.**

Ms. Discenza, known as the Founder and former Publisher of the successful monthly **Preemie Magazine**, understands the need of today's preemie parents to be able to grasp medical information in layman's terms and to be able to create a "new normal" in the midst of the NICU chaos. She also realizes the incredible challenge for new Preemie Parents to connect with the parenting world at large, as having a preemie is vastly different than a full-term baby.

During her tenure with the award-winning **Preemie Magazine**, Ms. Discenza was sought after for a variety of speaking engagements and media and news-related spots that address the medical community as well as the general public.

Therefore, Ms. Discenza has worked in the past decade plus with involvement in a variety of preemie-focused groups such as the Preemie Coalition, Operation Preemie, Preemies Today, PreemieCare and Mothers of Supertwins (MOST). From 2003 - 2014, Ms. Discenza was a walker and ongoing volunteer for the National Capital Area Chapter of the March of Dimes for the March for Babies, raising thousands of dollars to support the charity's good works in helping families and ongoing research. Today, Ms. Discenza is connected to and volunteers regularly with NICU Parent Network (***www.NICUParentNetwork.org***) and its member organizations.

Ms. Discenza is also an eager advocate of educating professionals on ways to help families in the NICU and beyond. As such, she is a regular Column Editor for the *Neonatal Network Journal*, for Neonatal Intensive Care Magazine and for the Council of International Neonatal Nurses (COINN) newsletter. She was also asked to join a commentary in the April 2019 edition of the *Journal of Pediatrics*. When not writing she is an international speaker at conferences and meetings for healthcare organization, industry and larger media.

In addition to PreemieWorld, Ms. Discenza has also launched Crystal Ball Health

with the first project being Preemie Crystal Ball, a global registry for the preemie community from birth into the geriatric years. Join the movement, share your preemie story or read more at ***www.crystalballhealth.com***.

In 2006, Ms. Discenza received an award from the **National Perinatal Association** for her work in supporting families during the NICU journey.

Prior to her work in the preemie community, Ms. Discenza was Senior Vice President for **Thruport Technologies** and **digitalNATION, Inc.** as well as Associate Publisher for **HostingTech,** an award-winning technology magazine.

She resides with her family in Virginia.

Becky Today, Age 16
Photo Credit: Deb Discenza

Deb Today *Photo Credit: Martin Lee*

NOTES:

preemieworld

PREEMIEWORLD is YOUR WORLD:

Go to ***PreemieWorld.com*** to read up on our newsletters, freebies, our calendar and infamous "Preemie Directory" full of content just for YOU.

While you are there, subscribe to your go-to newsletter: preemieFAMILY.

INSPIRE PREEMIE COMMUNITY:

(lead by Deb Discenza)

Join over 50,000 parents of preemies on this safe space just for us. Whether you are a parent of a baby in the NICU, at home, at school, or you are an adult born early - we are here for you.

Go to https://preemie.inspire.com.

PREEMIE CRYSTAL BALL:

Preemie Crystal Ball is coming . . . to improve research, improve outcomes in a way that benefits everyone - especially the preemie community from birth into the geriatric years.

#JoinTheMovement and ***#ShareYourPreemieStory*** at ***www.crystalballhealth.com***